To Diana

A Modern Woman's Guide to Aging:

Together We Consider Our Options

Truly a find

Claire Haye

Goddess!

Clai

A Modern Woman's Guide to Aging By Claire Haye

June, 2015

Copyright 2015 by Claire Haye

www.amodernwomansguide.com

Photographs by Lenny Foster (www.lennyfoster.com)

ISBN 978-1-63110-160-1

Printed in the United States by
Mira Digital Publishing
Chesterfield, Missouri 63005

My appreciation

for the wonderful guidance and support:

My book would have never happened without the encouragement, lunches with and expert editing by Sally Wasowski or the energy and talent of Carolyn Schlam.

Thanks also go to: Jane Bowes, Donna Donn Broughton, Mya Coursey, Lenny Foster, Phaedra Greenwood, Memphis Holland, Tristan Lee, Rebecca Lenzini, Laura Lynch, and Ted Wiard.

Contents

Introduction

Sunday. Cold and clear – the sky fierce blue. Snow on the ground. A spectacular winter morning. I was invited to my daughter Melissa's house for a family gathering. I cautiously drove the seven mountain miles from my home to her country home.

Last night's fresh snow crackled under my boots as I walked from my car to Melissa's front door. It was unlocked. Silent. I wandered in and removed my jacket and hung it on a hook. Unannounced, I went into the kitchen where Melissa was making crepes. She stopped cooking and looked hard at me for a long still moment, her grey eyes wide in her beautiful pale face. My daughter spoke, "When you came in, I was frightened." She paused, "I thought you were Grandma Bea.... Really, you looked just like her."

My god. Melissa thought I was my dead mother. Grandma Bea had taken leave of us twenty years ago. Unsettled, I grumbled to myself, "*There it is. Much to my surprise and even my dismay, I have become my mother.*"

Last week, I went to a party as fine as I could make myself, all groomed and glossy. No one took notice of me. What I really mean is none of the men looked at me. I had become oddly invisible to them. The message is significant, the reality unavoidable. Claire the Sex Goddess has left the room. Indeed, I am transforming into an old woman.

Consider my situation: I am a woman alone, healthy, a self-employed artist with my own gallery, grown daughters, sons-in-law, grand-children, a beautiful home, a functioning car. Yes, my life seems solid and comfortable—nothing to be concerned about, except creating new jewelry designs each year and a lingering hope for a last romance.

Now that most of my life has been lived, with my youth and my middle age behind me, what am I missing or avoiding in my self-portrait? Why is there an alligator in the bathtub? Where did I hide the key to the buried treasure? Who ate the missing piece to the jigsaw puzzle?

I understand that there are givens that I cannot escape. My genes have programmed me to age in certain ways. I have the accumulation of the particular life I have led, the stress and how I dealt with the stress, the food eaten, the commitment to exercise or not, the smoking or not, the alcohol and drugs taken, the environment lived in and the luck (unexplainable events or circumstances) or lack of luck in my life. All these things affect my expiration date.

The truth is: I am aging and will continue to age. Before I paint my last canvas, I will experience the deterioration of many of the physical systems that have kept me a fully functioning and quite independent person.

What will my last chapter be like? How will the aging process affect my ability to be self-determining and active? What can I do to stay vital? Can I afford to get old? These are important questions for all mature women to ask ourselves.

We might hope for a pill, or an injection, or an operation that would prevent us from becoming elderly or would give us back our youth.

We might hope. Scientists are researching the biological process in attempts to halt or even reverse aging. Considering the profit to be made, science may soon come up with some tangible answers. My cynical opinion is that expensive magic pills, or fantastic blood replacement schemes insuring permanent youth, will be available only to an elite- the same elite that now controls the majority of the world's assets. Most of us, certainly most women, will have to manage our own aging experience with diet, exercise, cosmetic adjustment, social outreach, purpose or spiritual belief, and preventive medical and dental care.

Yes, I acknowledge that I will fade and pass away. My consciousness of my own inevitable physical decline and eventual death was a powerful motivator in my writing this book. I have accepted that as I grow older, I am more and more like my mother. Grandma Bea had a long and juicy life. She dwelled alone in an elegant Manhattan apartment. A former dancer, she taught until the week before she died. Until the very end, she kept her curiosity, her will, and her ability to balance her checkbook. I am awed by her resilience. I have decided it is an excellent thing to mirror her as I wise.

In the process of researching and writing *A Modern Woman's Guide to Aging: Together We Consider Our Options*, I have become acquainted with some very dry, not to mention depressing and headache-inducing material. I have chosen to spare you any footnotes or graphs. For those of you who are interested in these topics and wish to learn more, I have included suggested readings at the end of each chapter. In addition, the appendix contains a bibliography- just to establish my sincere desire to acknowledge my debt to other authors. I wish to share what I have learned with my fellow travelers. However, this assemblage of stories, ideas, and information is meant to be an investigation/inquiry, not a "how-to" or a proselytizing book. I am hopeful that you will use this Guide as part of your own search for self-understanding and direction. There are pages to journal in with generous space for you to explore your personal issues and insights. *The Modern Woman's Guide to Aging* is here to encourage you to think about your life, ask important questions, make choices and find answers.

I invite you to journey with me.

Chapter One: What is Aging?

When we think of wine aging, we really mean that it is ripening to its full potential of flavor and bouquet—that moment of perfection just before it teeters towards undrinkable.

When we talk about a living being aging, we are referring to senescence—the final stage of the normal life span. Senescence is the state of physical deterioration that precedes death.

Because I am a senior citizen, I have passed through infancy, childhood, adolescence, young adulthood, and middle age. Next is old age and death. Can this be happening to me? Wow! How shocking to think that I am standing before the gateway to the last phase of my physical existence.

While I appreciate the gifts that maturity brings, I also mourn the passing of time. As a modern woman, I am living in a society that exalts youth and its attendant vigor, sexuality and potential. Youth has not always been worshipped as it is today. In the past and in more traditional cultures, women who achieved old age gained a natural respect in their society. Of course I want the esteem of my family, my peers and my society. Truthfully, though, it seems up to me to find self-worth and joy as I age.

Women are more likely to become old than their male partners, friends and relatives. Human females persist beyond their ability to have children. I find it moving and humbling that we have evolved to live beyond motherhood. We are one of the very rare female mammals that live past their ability to procreate. Only lady whales, female orangutans and women are members of this select club.

Women's extended lives beyond reproduction offer an evolutionary advantage. *Homo sapiens* is a highly acculturated, intensely languaged and teaching primate species. The stories, information and awareness of natural cycles, the special knowledge and specifically, the long view that an elder population can provide all of this learning has increased the survival rate of the species. Children with grandmothers have prospered more than children without. Gradually the descendants of these grandmothers have increased the longevity of the human species.

As a mature woman, you have no doubt observed that as you get older there seem to be fewer and fewer men. Women live longer than men—an average of five to ten years. The guys who endure the obstacle course of being male and make it to 75 and beyond are exceptionally hardy.

Imagine a Truman Capote moment: New Year's Eve, Manhattan, the Plaza Hotel, a fancy dress ball with the theme of white on white, a New Year's Eve Party exclusive to centenarians (folks 100 years old and over). There would be very few gentlemen. Four out of five of the celebrants would be decked out in high heels, pearls and low-cut pale dresses, smiling ladies with red lips, rouged cheeks and blue eye shadow.

It seems unfair that women live longer than men. Even mysterious. There are several random factors contributing to the longer life of the fairer sex. One possible cause of our longer life expectancy could be that during our menstruating years, because we bleed, we have less iron in our system. Lower levels of iron seem to reduce vulnerability to heart disease and may also be the reason why studies show that vegetarians or people who do not eat red meat live longer. During male puberty, testosterone increases male aggression. Men commit more than 70 percent of all murders. Auto insurance costs more for men than women, because the statistics based on male driving records warrant higher rates. Yes, men are dangerous to themselves and others. In addition, testosterone raises their unhealthy cholesterol level. This hormone also suppresses the male immune system, so they catch more diseases. Women are better able to create social connection. And women may have a built-in genetic advantage.

Stop here . . .

Yes, my Russian Great-Uncle Abe (what a mustache he had and a full head of hair) lived to be 95, smoked cigars, ate red meat, considered salad frivolous, never exercised, and enjoyed hard liquor. Uncle Abe had a paunch, flirted with the ladies, and pinched the cheeks of all the young pretty girls. And he managed to die at home in bed in his sleep.

Isn't it wonderful that individual vitality is not predicable? Researching and studying large groups of human populations provides an overview or map that does not always fit our personal experience. Rather it informs a bigger "truth" about configurations and expectations. Even so, our unexplainable human variety is a gift that science cannot take away from us.

Well, then, why do women live longer than men? Are women superior to men?

We are genetically different than men. What makes us girls is the female sex-determining chromosome XX (one X from Mom and one X from Dad.) What makes the boys male is the chromosome configured XY (one X from Mom and the Y from Dad.)

However, the Y is practically blank. The Y chromosome contains 27 genes mostly devoted to producing maleness, while the X has more than 500 genes.

The lack of genes on their Y makes the males very vulnerable to the genes that they inherit from mom. Thus conditions such as hemophilia, color blindness, fragile X syndrome, muscular dystrophy, and some forms of autism are much more common in men. Gentleman, choose your mothers carefully!

Now the big surprise: women get to use the genes on both their X's—all 1100 genes. During early gestation, groups of cells randomly choose to express the genes from Dad's X, and other groups of cells choose to express the genes from Mom's X. This creates a genetic mosaic all over the female body and more choices in the embodiment of traits. Think of the female Calico Cat—the variety of color in her fur is a display of this genetic difference. Meow.

Although you cannot necessarily see it or, indeed, you are not aware of it, the fact that you as a woman have a greater genetic mixture than men may give you better odds or biological options than most men. And a longer, if perhaps lonelier, life.

Of course, all women age! However, we all age at different rates, and different parts of our bodies seem to have their particular vulnerabilities to the process. My mother Pinky (aka Grandma Bea)—a dancer, a teacher and a serious Narcissus—took great care to remain youthful in her appearance. Pinky never looked her age. She looked simply marvelous. However, when she was in her seventies, Pinky went to the ophthalmologist. After the exam, which revealed that my mother's eyes had advanced cataracts, the doctor commented, "Madam, you may look fifty, but your eyes are eighty."

When I began to think about my own aging/dying process, I wondered if it would be possible to determine how much time I had left before I would leave the party.

How long will Claire live? I asked Google, and you can, too.

I used the resources of the Internet, including life insurance actuary tables. I answered questions about my grandparents, my habits, my weight and my height. Almost entirely honestly. Various sites produced life expectancies ranging from 82 to 93 years.

I averaged all the life expectancies. If I accept the validity of this process, I will die when I am 85. The very same age as my mother, Grandma Bea, passed on. Hmmmmm . . .

Do I then have only 18 years (and how many "good" years?) left to learn to control my temper, paint a masterpiece, visit far-off places, achieve enlightenment, and love those I love?

My journey towards death (unless cut short by an accident, murder, war, natural disaster, or suicide) must involve at least some of the deterioration that accompanies aging, no matter how carefully and diligently I have thought positive thoughts, taken vitamins, exercised, meditated or dieted.

I do not want to talk about it. I do want to talk about it. I want to know and I do not want to know.

Be advised, this chapter makes a serious effort to review the normal biological processes that occur in all women as time accumulates. I have done my very best to relay this material in a straightforward, concise, even friendly manner. You will have to decide if you want this information or not.

There are small groups of people who live close to the maximum life span of our species—which is... drum roll... 115 years.

You may have your own "Uncle Abe" or a grandparent or a neighbor—folks you know who age well. There are seniors who amaze everyone by dancing for hours at their great-grandson's wedding or who successfully take up skiing at 75. These are the natural long-lifers. They are just fine past the point where most people are either dead or very infirm. When these special ancient ones are near their end time, they exit after a brief decline. Super seniors. However, no matter how exceptional their journey seems to the rest of us, their autopsies show they have perished of the expected things: heart disease, cancer, etc.

And surprisingly, although your death certificate may very well declare that you had a fatal heart attack, your autopsy would reveal that you had multiple systems within your body that were in serious trouble. Remarkably, your autopsy might expose the presence of cancer, severe organ decline, and other items on the menu of aging.

This is me. This is you. We are getting older. Our bodies are waning. We each have our own schedule, and each of us experiences senescence in our own way. However, we all share this inevitable progression as we march or run or stroll down the path to death. The journey ends.

However, we do have options when it comes to the "how" we will age. After all my investigation, reading and research, I know I can to some extent prolong my vigor and gracefully inhabit my last years. Chapters 2 through 5 will consider strategies to battle or balance the physical and mental challenges of the last stage of our life.

Acceptance of your own natural pattern is, of course, your choice. Whatever your path, I encourage you to take a tough look at what physically happens to the average female body over a lifetime.

Contemplating what it means to grow old has made me unsure if I am brave enough to go the distance. I am at this moment healthy and mobile. I do not like the look of what is ahead.

Let us take courage from each other and boldly consider the tangible and common changes to the body as it becomes old.

THIS IS WHAT IS HAPPENING IN THE AGING PROCESS:

1. Our cellular energy declines.

The essence of the final stage of life is that our very cells are getting elderly and preparing for our death.

The fundamental 'why' of aging is taking place at the cellular level. We may look quite youthful thanks to self-care, medical science and cosmetic tinkering, but our cells are without any doubt getting tired.

Each of a woman's cells (as do men's cells) has a permanent symbiotic visitor—a nonhuman bacteria (the mitochondria) that lives with us and manufactures the energy we need to live. Yes, each of us is totally dependent for our life force on bacteria that live in our cells.

And every human being inherits these bacteria from just their mother. The smaller sperm (DNA and a tail) is designed for speed. Therefore, it is the large egg that is carrying the mitochondria. Only the mother gives her personal bacteria (think the "energizer") to all her offspring- male or female. Gives new meaning to Mother's Day.

Three major things are occurring in our cells as time accrues. Tick-tock.

1. Our cells' energy-making machines (mitochondria) are

14

diminishing in their number and their ability to manufacture energy

2. Garbage in our cells (free radicals) is gumming up the works.

3. Our telomeres (the tips of the genes) are getting shorter. You were lucky to be born a woman. Women, in general, have longer telomeres than most men. The telomeres protect the end of your chromosomes, but each time your genetic information is duplicated in the normal process of cell renewal, you lose part of the tip or telomere. Your chromosomes are getting frayed and less accurate. Your cells are finite because as they are replaced, they are losing the power for perfect future reproduction. Weakened and weary, our cells reach the end of their lifespan.

The result is that these changes affect what energy we have available. Aging cells lessen our body's ability to perform and to heal. Old cranky cells make old cranky women.

2. Our muscles get weaker.

During our young adulthood, we naturally continue to gain muscular strength. Then we reach a plateau, and our strength begins to decline. At 28, the human body has found its ultimate expression. The top of the mountain. After reaching our zenith, our bodies begin to break down and slide down the slope to death. None of us want to hear that news. Peak performance for most, but not all athletes, occurs before 30.

Endurance sports are more an extreme mental challenge than an apex of physical effort. Diana Nyad, a long-distance not a speed swimmer, continues to break records in her sixties. She swam from Cuba to Florida—

110 miles of ocean waters infested with poisonous jellyfish and sharks. Our Nyad, goddess of deep water, we applaud you for your achievements and see you as an exceptional woman and athlete who models for us how to go the distance.

Of course, the average women's life does not require the athletic performance of an Olympic competitor, nor does the average women of any age expect to achieve fame for her prowess in diving, gymnastics, rowing, or field and track. My life as a woman has had its own physical challenges. Mothering two daughters, born 19 months apart, felt like a marathon I had not properly trained for.

You may find yourself cursing in the kitchen when you cannot twist open the lid on the pickle jar. It is not the fault of the technology. Our hand strength is weakening. Lessening of our hand's proficiency may also signal changes in our heart and is an indicator of failing vitality. This gives a very specific meaning to "losing your grip."

For all women in all societies and occupations, as the years and the decades go by, our lack of muscular strength begins to affect the more ordinary activities of ordinary women.

Loss of muscle mass, strength, and mobility, along with general weakness, result in increased likelihood of falls, including those dreaded ones causing broken bones and hips.

3. Our bones are fragile.

Women are more vulnerable to osteoporosis than men. In general women have smaller bones than men. Slender women are at a greater risk for bone loss than their plumper friends. After menopause we no longer produce the hormones that have been protecting our skeletons from bone loss.

As women age, our bones become thinner and weaker, and the risk for broken hips, spine, and wrists becomes greater. And this is happening silently, as we shrink in height.

My mother the dancer, Pinky, was always confident. In memory of her former athletic self, at 66 years of age she was emboldened to try my friend's skateboard. She broke her wrist. When I was 66, I also broke my wrist. It happened while crossing a wooden plank over an irrigation ditch, thinking about joining a dating website, rather than watching where I was putting my sandal clad feet.

I wrote this poem after breaking my wrist. Skip it if you hate poetry. Many do.

What does come before a fall?

If I had just stepped firmly on the path

If there had been someone to hold my hand

If my guardian angel had been on duty

If I had stopped to catch the light slanting on the trees

If just then a dog had barked loudly or a cow snorted

If I had worn different shoes

If I had stopped rushing to please

If there had been someone to say, "Take care!"

If I had looked down and not inward

If I had listened to my heart

What does come before a fall?

Our fragile bones may be silently cracking and breaking. We may experience a terrible shock. We may "mysteriously" crash to the floor. Did we fall and break our hip? Or did our delicate bones give way, and that caused the incident? Our bodies have changed, and we were not properly notified.

Eight of the ten older people who break their hips are female.

Twenty percent of women who break a hip will die in the year following the initial accident. The reasons for this are not entirely clear to the medical establishment. Perhaps this one significant event-"The Fall" is communicating that the entire body is beginning to wear down.

-4. Our senses are dulling.

As we become older we will not hear as well or see as clearly. Our sense of taste will lessen. Flavors will pale. The odors of the world, nasty or pleasant, will lose their intensity.

The most common and the most known effect of aging for our eyes is cataracts. The lens in the eye becomes cloudy, which affects vision. Eventually, if not treated, cataracts result in blindness. Fortunately, there are wonderful and generally successful surgeries to correct this condition.

You may not be aware that you are losing your depth perception or your ability to distinguish colors. It may be quite obvious to you that you are losing your ability to focus on tiny print. In addition, you are becoming more sensitive to glare. Your older eyes will have more difficulty in adjusting from light to dark. No wonder driving at night has become more stressful.

Those loud rock 'n 'roll concerts did not help, but as you age, your ears and the delicate equipment in them ages. It is normal for everyone who lives long enough to hear less well.

"What did you say?" Check it out. It might be impacted earwax. More likely it is something else you are going to have to learn to live with— permanent loss of hearing, especially in the high frequency registers.

Your senses of taste and of smell are not as acute. Suddenly most food may seem quite flavorless. Trying to spice things up? Are you adding more salt, pepper or chili sauce? Be gentle with the perfume bottle. Less is more when it comes to sweetly scented old ladies.

You are most welcome to say you did not see, hear, smell, or taste this information.

5. Our cardio-vascular system is deteriorating.

Heart disease and its companion stroke are the number one killers of women over 65.

More women than men die of heart attacks. Especially after menopause, more women are felled by coronary events.

Our arteries are full of junk, and they are getting stiff and dangerously narrow. The walls of our veins are thinning and losing elasticity. Our blood pressure goes up. Suddenly we have varicose veins. We will never voluntarily wear shorts again. The decline of the circulatory system is the failing part of our aging body that is most likely to kill us.

A heart attack is a very bad moment in which the heart is deprived of its necessary blood supply. Without blood supply, your heart cells perish. Heart cells cannot be replicated. A coronary leaves your heart permanently damaged. A stroke (caused by a blood clot in the deteriorating arteries) is like a power outage in the brain. A part of your brain has died. You will never be quite the same person.

Yes, you can do many things to reduce your risk of heart disease and stroke. Chapters Two through Five consider ways to improve our quality of life.

6. Our chances of getting cancer increase.

These statistics might give you a heart attack: after age 65 the likelihood of your getting cancer is close to four times greater than it was for you at 25 years of age. The most frequent cancers that kill us are breast, colon, lung and stomach cancers. Of course, you were dying to know this.

In the young-old (65 to 79), cancer is the most likely exit line. Advancing age is a high-risk factor for cancer with persons over 65, accounting for 60 percent of newly diagnosed malignancies and 70 percent of all cancer deaths. This means if you do not die of a stroke or a heart attack, then cancer may give you a ticket out of town.

Have you lost a friend or family member to cancer? I have.

Sadly, for me, the statistics have names: Joan, Laura, Vedon, Lisa, Pozzi and Feeney. Farewell. Gone, gone...gone.

And hopeful congratulations to the tough and/or lucky survivors who have conquered their cancer: Deborah, Patricia, Anita, Rebecca, Mary, Veronica, and Claire. Yes, I am a cancer survivor.

Why the chances of getting cancer increase as we age is something of a mystery. One of the causes may be the failure of our immune system to ring the biological alarm system and sweep the earliest malignant cells from our bodies. The latest advances in science are beginning to address the puzzle of some cancers by using the patient's own immune system to cure their cancer. Stayed tuned . . .

You may not want to read any further. After all I have told you about the most likely cause of your demise, however, you may find the following information fascinating—I did. Onward.

7. Our immune systems are retiring.

Besides this increased risk of cancer as you age, there are other problems caused by the failure of your immune system to work effectively.

Aging lessens your ability to heal. As an older woman, you are less able to fight off infections. Aging increases your likelihood of autoimmune diseases. Increased inflammation in the body makes vaccines less effective and colds harder to get over.

Throbbing arthritis, inflaming your joints and robbing you of physical flexibility, is considered an autoimmune disease. Your immune system is attacking you from within your own body. The white blood cells are overreacting, imagining a threat. This false message sends white blood cells unnecessarily to your joints, making them swollen, stiff, red and painful. Arthritis is more common in the elderly and more common in old women than in old men.

Our adrenal glands are shrinking (from all the stress of a long life?), and in the elderly they may have shrunk so much as to be undetectable. This might be another part of why our immune system is flagging.

Type 2 Diabetes is considered an autoimmune disease. The risk of developing Type 2 Diabetes increases as you get older. Your lower muscle mass, lack of exercise, and weight gain contribute to your susceptibility to diabetes. Diabetes contributes to your risk for heart disease and stroke. This is a circle dance that involves failure of multiple physical systems.

Last year, I noticed white patches on my olive-skinned face—vitiligo—the skin disease that Michael Jackson famously did not have. It has no specific cause, but it is an autoimmune disease. My aging skin cells have dementia. They can no longer remember what to color me.

The point being that as a young-old person, my immune system is obviously no longer functioning as well as it once did. And this is happening to all of us as we age.

I know you are eager to continue reading this information. Or is it time for a light snack?

8. Our chemistry changes.

When you and I were young girls about to bloom into women, our bodies began to prepare us to attract partners, to procreate, and to nourish our offspring. Males responded to our bodies.

As our bodies prepare to die, we begin to fade, and so often along with this does male interest. The body begins to shut down the chemical factory that made us flower, kept our bones strong and sustained our vigor for decades.

The good news: we no longer have to worry about unwanted pregnancies. We are no longer "cursed"—a very telling and old-fashioned way to describe menstruation. Our vaginas are aging. Our hormones are disappearing. The loss of estrogen and progesterone may affect us by making us less juicy and ready or able to enjoy sex.

Estrogen and progesterone are the hormones that we lose when we experience menopause. When they disappear, so does much of our radiance. With the sparkle goes our protection against heart disease. We become more vulnerable to bone loss and brain shrinkage. Treating women with HRT (hormone replacement therapy) is controversial. Let us continue this conversation in Chapter 5.

Hormones (produced by the adrenals, the pituitary, the hypothalamus, the pancreas, even the heart) are sending weaker signals. At the same time the individual organs in our body are getting more reluctant to respond to the hormonal signals from all sources.

You might compare your aging organs to an orchestra in which the conductor has arthritis and the musicians are growing deaf.

9. Our skin is getting tired.

Darker-skinned women have an advantage. The more melanin (pigment), the better. Golden girls of beach tan fame are at a disadvantage. Our skin, yes, our largest organ, is showing wear.

Most skin damage is due to the sun. Whether you wore a hat and sunscreen or danced naked outdoors at noon, the years accrue and your skin weathers.

Your skin is thinner and drier. It sags, is more likely to bruise, has less of a fat cushion, and is wrinkling and crinkling. Your skin may exhibit skin tags, discoloration and increased freckling. You are also at a higher risk for various types of skin cancers.

The taut dewy smooth skin of youth becomes a memory captured poignantly in an old photograph you find discarded in a box of ancient tax returns. Ahhh! You were lovely. Sadly, when you were a young woman you did not even think of yourself as beautiful.

10. Our teeth and gums are aging.

Our teeth are wearing down and may appear darker or discolored. Teeth cannot repair themselves. So a tooth once chipped, broken or missing needs the attention of the dentist. Nothing ages our facial appearance more than losing our teeth or having bone loss in our jaw. Are you losing your bite?

"Toothless" and "old" and "hag" are words easily combined.

As an older woman, you are more vulnerable to gum disease that is an inflammatory response to bacteria and plaque. Gum disease is much more of a threat to general health than was once commonly believed. The condition of your gums affects your entire body, including your heart. Gum disease may even be related to dementia. If your gums are badly inflamed and are retreating from your teeth, these conditions may be symptoms of inflammation prevalent in your entire body.

Good news: modern dentistry and your self-discipline can partner to keep your mouth healthy.

Consider skipping the following section, which discusses

dementia. I know I want to.

11. Our brain is becoming an antique.

Our brain is much more able to change and grow than we once thought. We continue to create new brain cells through our entire lives. We are capable of learning and thinking in new ways at any age. Women and men have the best gift nature could give us ~ the large brain of *Homo sapiens.* We can use and develop our brain, as long as it remains healthy, and as long as we are alive. The educated brain stays young and healthy longer. Best advice: keep learning.

However, as we age, we are increasingly vulnerable to dementia and to Alzheimer's disease—something that rightly deserves to be feared. A death before death.

Alzheimer's disease starts as mild glitches and tangles in the brain, which eventually leads to total loss of memory and personality. It will take away what makes us an individual, thinking person. And we do not yet know how to prevent or cure it. We can just watch it progress.

Truth: I do care about grey hair, the loss of hormones and fragile bones. I miss my waistline. What scares me? Losing my judgment, memory, and sense of self.

My parents, Pinky and Heinz (divorced when I was two), reached their eighties without dementia. Although each had begun to struggle with some of the aspects of their daily functioning, both Pinky and Heinz managed to be aware and to be themselves. To the very end. I, at least in this one way, want to emulate them.

Women are at greater peril than men for dementia, in part because women live longer, and Alzheimer's disease risk rises with age. Two-thirds of the people with Alzheimer's are women.

If you are 65 or younger, your chances of having Alzheimer's are low. However, by the time you are 75, your chances have quadrupled. This means that out of every hundred women aged 75, about fifteen of the ladies will show some symptoms of—or even develop full-blown—dementia. And the odds get worse for you if you live another decade.

It is difficult and quite depressing to contemplate that 40 percent of 90-year old women will not know that they have lost their way.

Here's hoping that you and I are in the alive/awake/aware group of old birds. In our nineties, we will meet for lunch to discuss global warming, our diminishing funds and our plan to take over the government.

Seize the moment. The "now" is sacred. Engage fully. Do what you need to do. Know yourself. Set your goals. Direct your will power. We are alive and living fully.

Focus.

12. Strange things are happening to our precious bodies.

As we age, our bodies change in ways that are not necessarily life threatening, but can be annoying and/or upsetting. Graying or thinning of our hair is certainly one of the signs that our body is aging.

We are drying up. Our bodies contain 10 to 20 percent less water than they did at birth. We are experiencing a reduced sense of thirst. Old age is like being lost in a desert. We cannot see to find the oasis. And if we find the oasis, we have lost the desire to drink from the cool water.

Women may get hair on their chinny chin-chin and less on their female parts.

We may sound different as our voices develop a shaky or trembling quality. Truly our voices sound muffled. Helllloo deearry!

Our digestive systems are no longer carefree. Many of us will experience some type of digestive problem. Hence the expression "Old Fart."

Our bladder muscles are weaker. We may be prone to urine leakage. Time to Kegel (exercises for the pelvic floor to reduce urinary incontinence.) Contract. Release. Contract. We will have to quietly exercise our sphincter muscles so we won't pee in our pants when we laugh too much.

Sleep problems are common for the vintage woman. If we can fall asleep then we may wake up several times in the night. At dawn, we may find ourselves alert, ready to feed a newborn baby that grew up a long time ago and is now going bald.

After 60, four out of ten women (compared to six out of ten men) have become noisy sleepers. The Master poses the koan: "The grand-mother sleeps alone in her bed. The dog died. The cat ate the bird and then ran away. There is no other person in the house. The house is in the forest. Is Grandma snoring?"

We are less able to tolerate changes in temperature. We get more easily chilled and more easily overheated.

As we become quite old (eighty and beyond) ~ our personal smell will be different and will identify us as old even if we hide many of the other visible markers of aging.

Enough!

Like you I am a mature woman. My uncompromising look at the biological process called senescence is just one of the ways I want to con-sider the final phase. I am lighting candles, dancing to sacred music, and waving ribbons of colored silk.

Most of the data I have gathered about the aging process is unwelcome news. Yes, I have grieved over certain tough morsels of infor-mation that predict the waning of my once lovely body and agile mind.

And you . . . Do you feel secure in your ability to meet all the physical challenges of getting older? Or are you concerned about your ability to cope with the inevitable changes to come?

You may say: "I can accept the decline of my body and I am fine with whatever life brings me." I am not like that. My contemplation of what it truly means to get old has convinced me to take some actions to amend this phase of my life. I wish to share the useful information I have gathered.

Join me in my journey.

Continuing the Conversation

Suggested Reading:

"What is aging?" is definitely the chapter with the heaviest amount of information on biological processes. You may feel that I needed to establish my scientific authority with footnotes and other data. For the doubting Judy, I recommend you read several excellent resource books that will corroborate the information that I have included in the guide.

How We Die: Reflections on Life's Final Chapter, written by Sherwin Nuland, published by Vintage Books.

This was the first book I read about aging and dying. Just after my mother died, when I was morosely wandering the streets of Manhattan, it seemed every bookstore in the city had this book prominently displayed in their windows. Timely. A winner of the National Book Award, it is a classic in its genre. For all of us who wish to come to terms with aging and dying, this book provides information, empathy and comfort. Nuland is a distinguished surgeon and a fine scientist, but he never discards his human heart or his own emotional reactions. A fascinating read.

How and Why We Age, written by Leonard Hayflick, Ph.D., published by Ballantine Books.

This is a very technical book with an academic tone. There is no shortage of graphs, charts, footnotes and bibliography. Not light reading, but still a wonderful and interesting guide to the science of aging. Well-researched and complete.

Physical Change and Aging: A Guide for the Helping Professions written by Sue Saxon, Mary Jean Etten & Perkins, published by Springer Publishing.

These three female authors have scrupulously eliminated any sense of their personalities from this guide as well as any emotion about aging. Nevertheless, this is a thorough and quietly compassionate discussion of all aspects of getting old and dying. Much of the information that is in my guide is also in this book. However, my guide speaks directly to the actual aging woman, not to her caregivers. The in-depth discussion of the physical characteristics of the aging process, although dry, is readable and understandable. A great reference book.

More suggested reading especially for those who love science...
I realize that many of my readers are not as interested in genetics as I am. My   fascination with this subject began with an excellent biology teacher at the Bronx High School of Science. The following well-written books are for my readers who love science, especially genetics.

Adam's Curse: A Future Without Men, written by Bryan Sykes, published by Norton.

Although Bryan Sykes is one of the world's preeminent geneticists, he writes like a mystery writer. And so much of how genes work has been a big mystery until very recently. Sykes will unravel for you the peculiar and particular differences between men and women. Men and women are apparently quietly at war. Genetically.

Genome: The Autobiography of a Species in 23 Chapters, **written by Matt Ridley, published by Harper Perennial**

This book is challenging but worthwhile. Ridley can explain in-depth and give clear meaning to difficult subjects. His chapter on death is an education that you may not have wanted. Occasionally, he is so enamored of a particular subject and squeezes so much information into one paragraph that the reader may not be able to digest it. However, this is a fascinating book taken in small bites.

Useful Websites:

You can visit my website to download any journals or forms that I have included in the guide. I will share anything new I learn about aging with frequent updates and thoughts.

www.amodernwomansguide.com

Truth: There is really no way that any formula can predict at what age you will die. The life expectancy that you calculate from these sites is simply an informed guess. However, I found that confronting myself with an actual end time age was a powerful experience. I felt viscerally the limits of my lifeline.

To help answer the question "How long will I live?", check out these sites:

gosset.wharton.upenn.edu/~foster/mortality
media.nmfn.com
time.com/3485579/when-will-i-die-life-expectancy-calculator/
www.socialsecurity.gov
www.free-online-calculator-use.com/life-expectancy-quiz.html

Check out these sites for all the latest information about aging and health.
Websites with good information about aging:

www.sharecare.com
www.healthinaging.org
www.mayoclinic.org

Analyzing your own aging process:
Is my body trying to get my attention?

After reading Chapter 1, you may want to look at your own aging process. Or not. This series of questions gives you an opportunity to think about your general health and vitality.

YOUR JOURNAL FOR SELF-UNDERSTANDING:

1. **MUSCLES:** How strong are you? Are you having trouble opening jars? Can you get up from the floor using just your leg strength and not your hands?

2. **BONES:** How strong are your bones? Have you had a bone density test? Have you broken any bones? Do the women or men in your family suffer from osteoporosis?

3. **SENSES:** How are your vision and your hearing? Have you had your eyes and ears tested? What is the family history?

4. **CARDIOVASCULAR SYSTEM:** Are you short of breath? Has anyone died of a stroke or heart attack in your immediate family? Had an electrocardiogram or stress test?

5. **CANCER:** Have you had cancer? Has anyone in your family had cancer? What type? Have you had a mammogram or a colonoscopy?

6. **SELF CARE:** Have you established a relationship with a doctor that you can call on if you have a health issue? Are your immunization shots up to date? Do you want flu shots? When was your last check-up?

7. **EMOTIONS:** Are you experiencing too much stress? Would joining a group help you deal with a long-standing problem? Do you need to talk to a professional about your issues?

8. **FEMALE:** Have you gone through menopause? Do the women in your family have any type of female problems? Have you had a recent Pap smear test? Are you on hormones? Are you practicing safe sex?

9. **SKIN:** Are you taking care of your skin? Have you seen a dermatologist? Do you use sunscreen? Daily?

10. **TEETH:** Are you friends with your dentist? Do you have good dental hygiene habits?

11. **BRAIN:** How is your memory? Having senior moments? What is your family history? Did a close relative suffer from dementia?

12. **PERSONAL:** What have you noticed about yourself that you think may be due to aging? Truthfully.

Review your answers. What do you feel about the state of your health? What are your conclusions?

Terrific, your health is excellent. You are aging without any effort.

Or... Ahhh, I am not so sure my health is so great!

If the latter is the case, consider doing something about the warning signs or even the odd messages that your body is whispering to you. You may need to pay attention to your body. Please consult Chapter 5 to get a handle on this subject. Chapter 5 has a great deal of information on doctors, dentists, and other healthcare specialists.

Thoughts.......

Thoughts.......

Thoughts.......

Thoughts......

Thoughts.......

Chapter Two: What is on my plate?

I understand that I have lived the majority of the years given as my normal life expectancy. I want to make the most of my remaining vital years. Rather than being concerned with simply extending the years I inhabit my body, I will attempt to improve the quality of my life experience and, if possible, create a well-lit path that leads to a dignified and gracious exit.

After all my reading and research, I am quite willing to say that the answers to my quest to maintain a dynamic presence and stall off the aging process as long as possible can be put quite simply.

The main buffers to the unavoidable and irrefutable deterioration that accompany getting older are diet, exercise, connection, purpose, and preventive medical and dental care.

However, a generous and thorough discussion of what might ameliorate the aging process deserves our attention.

We humans are very curious. Why do certain people, and even certain groups of people, live long and stay vigorous? The hunt is on. Find these long-distance elders and distill their secrets so we can benefit from the answers. Pursuing this line of thought, I have read about pockets of these super seniors located all over the world. Quite a thrilling journey.

There is much to be learned from studying specific populations in Japan, Greece, Costa Rica, and even California that uncover how to succeed at getting old. It is often a combination of healthy food, strenuous work, limited amounts of calories, community, something in the water, hanging with your neighbors, eating your vegetables, a close family, and vigorous exercise.

Consider this lifestyle:

You are a 98-year-old woman who lives alone in a simple clean one -room hut in the mountains. You get up at first light and eat a small meal of yogurt and fruit. Every morning you sweep the room, chop some wood, and then bathe in the cold mountain stream. When your tasks are done, you sit in your chair, and drink a tea brewed from herbs gathered in the forest. Today you walk uphill five miles on a rough mountain path to visit your daughter. Your daughter and her husband are both 79 years old. This family threesome shares a lunch of goat meat soup, freshly baked bread, local wine and laughter. Alone, you walk home singing. For your dinner you eat cooked vegetables, cheese and bread. You wash the dishes in cold water. When night darkens your hut, you are ready to lie down on your hard, narrow bed. You sleep deeply and well.

Can you and I translate these lessons to our own lives?

How willing are you to depart from what is familiar, comfortable, comforting and usual—that is the lifestyle that you've been living, the food you've been eating, the amount you've been eating, and the activities that are normal for you? Will you live longer if you make major changes in diet and routine, or will it just *seem* longer?

For more than 20 years, I've been reading about restricted diets that have minimal—yet on the mark—nourishment. The research seems to indicate that this type of diet will extend your life and your youthfulness. Great! Wonderful! Put me in a well-enforced cage and feed me nutritious pellets.

CRON (Caloric Restriction with Optimum Nutrition) follows the lead of this research. A woman on this diet plan would need to eat only 1,300 carefully selected calories a day. What it means to live the life of a CRON is that you would have to think carefully about every tiny bite of food that goes in your mouth. For a "foodie" like me, choosing this path is like joining a religious group that believes in self-flagellation. The major proponent of this method, Dr. Roy Walford, was a well-respected scientist and author of *Beyond the 120 Year Diet*. In spite of adhering to a strict food plan, he only made it to 79.

To be fair, there is important and extensive research behind this dietary viewpoint. If you can balance the stress of minimal eating with the proven health benefits of eating light and right, this approach to anti-aging may seem the logical and appropriate path for you.

My husband, John Michael, was very disciplined about his diet. He needed to be because by the time he was 34, his coronary arteries were completely blocked. Even so, on a rare occasion he'd asked his mother,

Helen Audine, to serve up the family's favorite home-cooked meal. I never understood the appeal: dry, overcooked pot roast, gray string-beans hanging limply on the fork, mashed potatoes with margarine, white bread dinner rolls with more margarine, Jell-O mold, and chopped iceberg lettuce salad with your choice of bottled salad dressing. Sometimes, if Helen felt festive, she would slice up an ice cream roll. Hardly the Mediterranean diet. In spite of all his efforts, John Michael died when he was 57. His mother, Helen Audine, content with her white bread diet lived to be 91.

Food is not simply fuel. It is also mother love, party time, comfort, distraction, release, and reward. We learn our relationship to and our patterns around food early in our family life.

My father Heinz, born in 1902, starved in Germany after World War I. All he could find to eat were turnips, and he developed boils all over his body. But he survived. Years later, when I knew him, my father was quite fond of turnips, mashed with ample amounts of cream and butter. However, he was offended if I left food on my plate.

My mother Pinky, born in 1910, grew up in a poor immigrant family in Chicago. Her mother Sonja was crazy. Sonja the Mad would not allow her six children to go to bed if they had fever or colds. Sonja made them sit in chairs until they were over their illnesses. Until she was 50, my Aunt Pauline, the eldest daughter, never dared to have a cold. Sonja did not like to cook. According to my aunt, their mother fed her six children some undefined form of "soup" or gruel. My dear aunt took over the cooking and was, of course, well loved by all her siblings. My mother did not much want to talk about her childhood.

When I was a little girl, Pinky was still performing with her own dance company. My mother was quite obsessed with remaining thin. After all, she was not only my mother; she was the dancer, *Beatrice Von Stronstorff*. Pinky was not a morning person; breakfast was not something she did. So as a young child I rummaged in the refrigerator for my morning meal and ate what I found. The "what I found" ranged from olives and carrots to leftover lentils.

The point being, I have baggage around food that I have inherited from my parents, that the culture has modeled for me, and what my own experiences have provided. If I awaken my inner wounded hungry child, I find myself shaky, grumpy, and angry.

Do you have issues around food or your weight? Do you have serious problems focused on either your body and or dieting? Do you have an eating disorder? You might want to join a self-help group or start one. You may want professional help from a nutritionist or therapist or both. It is never too late to deal with our emotional challenges and find healing.

How helpful are diets for the average only slightly neurotic woman? Every year brings us many new and thrilling (thrilling because they promise us success) dieting plans and often a new food pyramid from the US Department of Health. I am confused. ***What should I eat and how much of it?*** And what if I do not like the answers?

I am old enough and often plump enough to have tried the Grapefruit Diet, the South Beach Diet, Dr. Sear's Zone Diet, the Atkin's Diet, and the truly dreadful Cabbage Soup Diet. I am a member of Weight Watchers. I have fasted and cleansed. Then there are the supplements and pills that I have purchased. Touted by celebrities and famous doctors, these exotic extracts claim to alter my eating patterns and/or my metabolism.

I have also eaten an entire pint of pistachio ice cream by myself in one careless sitting.

What is thin enough?

The answer to this question for aging or elderly women is: ***not nearly as thin as you might think.*** We are pummeled by the media's tricked-up images of perfect-looking and extremely thin women—very few of them older than 22, or weighing more than 110 pounds or less than 5'9" tall. The average starved model has the proportions and height that can only be found in one in 10,000 women. Yet that is the standard we are held to.

Why can't the women in ads look more like us? We are the buying public. Let us reform the advertising industry—tomorrow. Today, what we are interested in discussing in this guide is increased health and optimal aging odds. How does weight affect our health?

As for myself: what should Claire weigh?

The pundits say the relationship between my weight and my height—the Body Mass Index or BMI—will tell me a great deal about my mortality risk and my health. To figure out your own BMI, all you do is divide your weight in pounds by your height in inches. Or just google BMI and plug in your numbers. Okay, Claire, what does this really mean?

Take me. Let's analyze my body mass index. At one time, I would have told you that I was 5'6" tall. I was delusional. Honestly, I am 5'4 3/4" tall and I weigh 150 pounds. How far from ideal am I?

My BMI says at 25.2 that I am slightly overweight (it is my breasts, I tell you) and that I probably should not put on any more weight. Furthermore, **if** I have other risks factors such as high blood pressure, diabetes, low HDL, high LDL, cannot fit in my favorite jeans, and would like to look better in a swimming suit, it would be really helpful if I would lose 10 percent of my body weight or 15 pounds.

Instead of being me (a very average-sized woman), what if am that 5'9", amazingly slender model. Now a senior citizen after my very successful modeling career, I have managed to stay thin. What if I still weigh 110 pounds? Would that be great? Besides being able to wear size 4 jeans, would I actually be healthy?

No, no, no. With a BMI of 16.1, I would be very likely to drop dead sooner than later. The elderly women who are underweight (a BMI of 19 and under) have a severely increased risk of mortality and a high rate of osteoporosis.

Now imagine me, Claire at my height, weighing 197 with a BMI of 29 (overweight and unpleasantly plump) but without heart disease, diabetes, high blood pressure, etc. Would I be unhealthy? No. While this seems so counter-intuitive, **I would have less risk of dying than the very thin, the average or truly obese.** Can you believe this? Strange. But would I like looking in the mirror? None of my clothes, including my "hide- anything" skirt, would fit.

Now envision me, Claire, at the same height but quite round. I have stopped moving and rarely get up from the couch or my desk. I skip breakfast. I lunch on fast food. I enjoy rich sugary snacks every evening just before bedtime. Fat Claire at 209 pounds with a BMI of 35 would have a significantly increased mortality. My chance of dying is up by 29%. I have an elevated risk of diabetes, a greater chance of arthritis, increased vulnerability to cancer and sleep apnea.

Another way of easily calculating your probability of health glitches, especially heart problems, is determining your waist-to-hip ratio. This self-evaluation is easily done: divide your waist measurement by your hip measurement. Honesty is best—no need to violently suck in your waist. If your hips are 39" and your waist is 29", then your ratio is 7.4.

According to some health gurus, the waist-to-hip ratio is a better indicator of your health than body mass index. One reason this may be true is that gaining weight in your middle around your vital organs is more dangerous than gaining weight on your hips or thighs.

If the ratio is less than 7, you have a low risk. My ratio of 8.5 suggests a moderate risk.

I gain most of my weight wrapped around my trunk. If, after a very enthusiastic holiday party-going season my waist does expand to over 33", then the ratio of my waist-to-hips will be over 9. Then I would be in danger of becoming very intimate with heart disease, diabetes, and high blood pressure. My mother, the dancing Pinky, even in her eighties had gorgeous legs, but carried all her extra weight in her mid-section. Pinky had chronic high blood pressure—and took her pink pills randomly. On May 1st, 1995, she died of a stroke.

I am ready to admit that I am at risk for a stroke. I want to lose that magic 10% of my body weight with the intention of improving my health and lowering my risk for stroke. How am I going to accomplish this? What would you do?

Weight loss hangs heavy on the hearts of modern women.

If we are ready to take on this challenge again (haven't we done this before?), we need to consider not just how much we eat, but also what we eat. And sometimes it is simply, "*What is eating me?*"

Let us also consider our long history as tribal human beings wandering around a sparsely populated planet.

Our modern lives in cities and suburbs complete with seductive techno marvels, restaurants, transportation, indoor plumbing, heated and cooled shelters is a thin overlay on eons of time when we lived a simple existence. For most of our stint on earth, bands of *Homo sapiens* roamed in natural settings. Our foods came from nearby. We gathered and hunted. There were lean times, and we starved. When there was plenty, we gorged. We tended to our wounds and illnesses with native herbs and prayer.

How does this ancient way of life affect us as modern women?

We are all descended from hunter-gathers who were omnivorous, opportunistic, and *not* picky eaters. The picky eaters died early and without offspring.

In regards to what foods we can be nourished on, humans are the opposite of panda bears whose diet is 99% bamboo plants. If bamboo becomes extinct, pandas become extinct. *Homo sapiens* can live in every climate zone of the world. Human beings have a fantastically adaptable, wonderfully versatile digestive system.

All of us are descended from generations of people who ate and survived on the diet that their culture and family offered them, whether it was seaweed and fish, kasha and cabbage, beans, chilies' and corn, or cassava and grubs.

The human diet for eons was **not** was a diet high in fat, loaded with sugar and full of dense, calorie-laden food in small packages, such as chocolate candy bars, cheese, potato chips, salami, energy bars, cherry pie or even granola. Regular meals were never certain for early humans. Sweet foods and foods rich in fat were very rare in our diet for millions of years, and difficult to find. Unfortunately, we are programmed to consume, with eager gusto, these once uncommon rich and/or sugary foods. Every fast food chain in America uses this evolutionary trait to fatten their bottom line.

When I succumb to ancient impulses or modern demons, and devour a pint of ice cream out of the container spoonful by spoonful without stopping until the ice cream is all gone, I have consumed 1200 calories, 170 grams of fat, 22 grams of carbohydrates and 20 grams of protein.

For the same calories I could have eaten a 9-ounce steak, a baked potato with butter and sour cream and a small Caesar salad. Or, I could have feasted on an East Indian dinner of chicken tandoori, dal, two samosas with chutney, rice, spinach and a cup of rose-scented rice pudding.

- How would you choose to spend your 1200 calories?

- And what if it was your last meal?

Time now for a short test. *True or false:*

- You should never eat any food that belongs to the nightshade family, which includes tomatoes, potatoes, eggplants, red, green, and chili peppers.

- All wheat is toxic and addictive.

- Women with Type-O blood should never eat wheat or seeds.

- Choosing non-fat foods over fat rich foods is a good way to control your weight.

- Eating salmon or sardines every day will keep your skin youthful and wrinkle-free.

- You should never combine starches and proteins in the same meal.

- Raw food is more nourishing and easily digested than cooked food.

- Diet Coke will make you gain weight.

- Women with Type-A blood should never eat steak.

- It takes more calories to eat a grapefruit than there are calories in the grapefruit.

- Many adult females have lost lactase, the enzyme needed to digest milk.

Hmmm.... Not sure what the right answer is?

And what is a perfect diet for a modern woman who wants to age well? Is there one food regime that will work for all of us? Don't you want a definitive answer to this important question? Is there a miraculous food plan? Well, let us take a peak at how three women deal with this issue.

SOPHIA'S WAY:

Here is Sophia C. She is a lovely 75-year-old, certainly, with her still dark hair and those curves, very sexy. She lives in New Jersey and still eats the old-style, traditional foods. These include:

A small serving of some type of lean protein

Vegetables cooked in olive oil

Salad with olive oil dressing

Fruit daily

Cheese

One daily serving of nuts

More olive oil

Pasta or rice

Capers

Olives

Bread

2 cups of coffee

Two glasses of red wine

An occasional cannoli

You may be nodding, "Yes, I would love to eat that food, live that life, be that sexy." Other women might be saying, "Where's the chicken potpie, the fruit smoothie, or the Reuben sandwich?" Anyway, not all of us would agree that this is the best food plan for health and youth.

•

Perhaps we could agree that the best anti-aging diet is the one followed by Sally.

SALLY'S FOOD PRACTICE:

Sally is one spritely 95-year-old lady in California who is still driving, going to church, exercising daily, and helping the less fortunate. We find Sally wearing a big flowery hat, motoring her Cadillac fast down Highway 10 on her way to help out at a Senior Center. She is a Seventh Day Adventist and religiously follows a strict diet:

Oatmeal and other grains

Vegetables

Plenty of nuts

Milk and other dairy products

Eggs

Only protein from vegetable sources

Water

And complete **abstinence** from chocolate, alcohol, coffee, tea, and all other caffeinated beverages

My first morning coffee often takes on the overtones of a sacred ritual. And how about that glass of cabernet sauvignon with dinner?

Some of us would agree to eat this way. Others would say, "No way! Too limited."

Here's one more plan to think about...

SARA GOES PALEO:

Sara is a very modern urban woman. Sara keeps up with the latest trends. She has decided to eat like her early ancestors. She is getting in touch with her inner hunter-gatherer. She believes that to be a lean, energetic, and feeling-like-getting-out-the-bow-and-arrow huntress, she should eat in a very specific manner:

Red meat: grass-fed

Fowl: chicken, duck, turkey, and pigeon—all free-range

Fish: wild-caught

Eggs: organic

Fruits and vegetables: all local

Seasonal wild greens: harvested under the full moon

Oils: olive, walnut, and sesame seeds—all stone-ground

Nuts: found in nearby forests

Tubers: sweet potatoes and yams

Herbal tea: made from leaves she gathered

And on special occasions (like returning triumphant from the hunt): wine or tequila

Avoiding and never eating: dairy, bread, pasta, grains, legumes, sugar and refined manufactured foods—really, never!

So, we might embrace this plan only to be waylaid by birthday cake.

The Big Truth: We cannot create a consensus on what is the proper diet for a human being. One "expert" may convince you to follow his/her eating scheme, but you can be certain another brilliant Ph.D. or M.D. will next year publish a different solution to weight control and optimum health. We are talking about a very profitable industry that makes billions and billions of dollars every year by convincing women to follow the food religion of the moment.

So, if we cannot agree on the ideal diet for health, weight loss or anti-aging, how can we choose our path through the forest of this contradictory information?

We can agree that, at any age, exercising more and eating less will change our body.

Let us consider our human nature. You have not been able to find an exorcist who will kill the demon that occasionally takes control of what you choose to eat—have you? Do you sometimes consume foods or food-like substances just for fun? Can we agree that you might just want to eat or drink and consume with a smile on your face: donuts with cream filling, chocolate cookies, fettuccini Alfredo, fried chicken, a strawberry milkshake, margaritas, eggnog, candy at the movies, pizza with three meats, French fries, a Big Mac, brie cheese and crusty French bread, sweet and sour shrimp with white rice, or bonbons while reading a trashy novel.

What is your favorite food "sin"?

We may be "forced" to eat or drink some of these bad for us, high-fat, high-sugar, high-calorie foods by hunger or a kind, persistent hostess or even by the devil. Does it really matter in the big picture of our health?

Moving on to a common perception:

Eat this food _____ and it will cure_____ and you will live to_____.

We might agree that there are foods that are amazingly good for you and good to eat: blueberries, dark leafy vegetables, wild-caught fish, avocados, almonds, oysters, apples, broccoli, cabbage, garlic, onions, Brussels sprouts, horseradish root, sauerkraut, yams, walnuts, dark un-sweetened chocolate, kumquats, quinoa, sardines, pomegranates, beans, chia seeds, carrots, figs, apricots, prunes, walnuts, mushrooms, oranges, red peppers, goji berries, Asian pears, eggs and yogurt.

You may never have heard of some of these healthy foods.

You may not like any of these foods, or just a few of them—or only want to eat them when the Moon is in Scorpio. What foods do you like to eat that make you feel like dancing in the street?

Wait a moment....

This is the ideal moment to present you with my diet plan. And to sell it to you hard. The very special menu that I invented that will keep us youthful, with glowing skin, perfect eyesight, healthy teeth and bones, increased muscle mass, and a sharper memory.

The Really Big Truth: *This diet does not exist.*

Huh?

How can I decide for myself what is a proper diet for my own wellbeing and happiness? Great question!

*What if **you** were in charge?*

How to begin? **Know thyself.**

You could make a considered self-assessment. At the end of this chapter (or at *www.awomansguide.com*), you will find a journal on which to record for 14 days what you eat, drink, how you feel about food, and any other information you can self-gather that might provide insight into the what, why, and how of your relationship to food.

I am asking you to witness yourself and to scrupulously record your observations.

I am recommending you stop trying to eat the way you think you should be eating and find out what you are actually eating. Yes, I am suggesting you stop trying to find the perfect diet and begin to understand how you feel about the food you eat and how the food you eat makes you feel.

When using the journal, it would be helpful if you were **honest** and **complete** in your information gathering. Consider all the factors in your personal life, write down exactly what you consume, what you are thinking and feeling when you are eating. Please regard your own food intake as neutrally as possible. Quiet your critic, your inner judge.

Just gather information. Creating this journal is not meant to be an exercise of will power. It is an exploration—a journey for self-knowing.   At the end of the 14 days, read every word of your journal.

I can hear some of you now: "**No.** I do not want to do this. I like what I eat, how much I eat, and when I eat. I do no not need to think about it." Fine, fine, fine. If you are happy, then I am happy for you.

But, I hope you will say, "*Yes.* This is a great idea, and I am going to work with my journal and fill out every space and answer fully and consciously all the questions."

Read what you wrote. Think about the information you gathered. What have you learned? How do you rate your own diet?

1. Wow, I could work for a spa! Excellent!
2. Reasonable, but I cannot believe I ate _____.
3. Shitty.
4. I think it is time to change.

What is your attitude towards taking care of yourself in regards to food choices? How could you improve the quality of your diet, the nutritional excellence and the enjoyment of what you ate? As the two weeks went by and you wrote about your personal relationship to eating, did you find any changes in your food consumption and selections? You may have discovered that you need help to resolve old and troubling issues. You may realize that you compulsively overeat or sternly restrict your food intact. It may be time to find a therapist or a group to deal with the emotional problems that show up as you contemplate your dual relationship with self and food.

You may complete the journal and then...

You might decide, after all, you have great dining habits. You are comfortable with what you normally consume. You either will take your chances with your health risks or you feel you are perfectly healthy—thank you very much.

Or, it may be obvious to you that your food and drink consumption could use some tweaking and judicious reconsidering. You have come to a decision: "I am going to change my relationship with food. I, in all honesty, know my body would function better if I released (you decide)_____pounds."

Remember the odd statistics I have unmasked. Being very thin is a health risk for older women. Remind yourself when you set your weight goal for yourself that you are no longer 40 or even 50 years old. Your weight as a senior should reflect the need for reserve fat. You can give up the ideal you set for yourself 20 years ago. Throw out those skinny jeans, finally back in fashion that you have hidden in your closet for 20 years.

Changing your food menu to increase your health and vitality is not necessarily dieting—although it may produce weight loss.

I am going to suggest to you that after all your years of reading on the fascinating subject of food, after your two weeks of food journaling, your many years of living in your body and your powerful intuition, that you can create your own wise woman, self-nurturing food and drink viewpoint.

If you have to consult a book with its resident expert, I recommend one very slim guide: *Food Rules* by Michael Pollen. I believe that you have the knowledge and the tools to construct a food and drink pattern that is perfect for you. Just for yourself. Your partner will be fine. Your partner is a grown person who can join you on your food plan or not.

The journal has a section for you to design your dining blueprint or compose a food strategy. Weigh yourself. Take your waist and hip measurements. Set real and realistic goals. Stay awake. Be conscious of how changing your eating habits changes your sense of self. At the end of the chapter, I have included some suggestions for managing your relationship with food.

Can we agree that we want to eat for life, well being, and pleasure? Remember your goal is to be your **healthiest self**, with energy for all you wish to accomplish. Create a personal nutritional regime and write it down in your journal. This is an eating plan that you have chosen and that you have created, that you feel is appropriate for who you are and who you want to be.

Truth: exercise will have to be part of the program if you are serious about transformation. In the following chapter, I have a great deal to say about moving your body.

Summon your courage, your will and your inner wisdom. Be kind and loving to yourself. **Eat right for yourself.** If you have a misstep, release the guilt and go back to your plan. If you have learned you need help with these issues, please seek guidance knowing you deserve to be whole and healed.

One day you will know that your body is in balance and that your relationship with food is wise. Please continue to eat with awareness, to journal and to exercise.

KNOW THYSELF, AND TO THY OWN SELF BE TRUE.

Continuing the Conversation

Suggested Readings:

The Blue Zones: Nine Lessons for Living Longer From the People Who've Lived the Longest written by Dan Buettner, published by National Geographic.

This book is an entertaining read. *The Blues Zones* takes you all over the world to meet elderly people. These are healthy and active old folks. Very charming. Great photos. Dan gives very sensible advice about diet and exercise. He also distills all that he has learned from groups of successful agers into this book. In *The Modern Women's Guide to Aging*, I reached the same conclusions as Buettner: "The main buffers to the unavoidable and irrefutable deterioration of the body are: exercise, diet, connection and purpose." The reader can decide if she wants to or has the ability to implement this information.

The Omnivore's Dilemma written by Michael Pollan, published by Penguin Books.

I counsel you to read any book written by Michael Pollan. Here is an author who thoroughly explores the relationship of humans to what they eat and how food affects our health. He shamelessly compares *Homo sapiens* to rats, because we share that marvelous characteristic of being able to eat and survive on almost any food. He talks a great deal about the perils of modern industrial farming and the pitfalls of the western diet. Michael Pollan is my hero. I like that he admits that he eats and enjoys all kinds of food. A great writer and a great read.

Food Rules: An Eater's Manual written by Michael Pollan, published by Penguin Books.

Michael Pollan (my food guru) has written a concise volume, which encompasses all you will ever need to know about what you should be eating. *Food Rules* is an amazing distillation of facts from a well-informed author. Very digestible. His words: "I realized that the answer to the supposedly incredibly complicated question of what we should eat wasn't so complicated after all, and in fact could be boiled down to just seven words: "*Eat food. Not too much. Mostly plants (my italics).*"

The Story of the Human Body, Evolution, Health, and Disease written by Daniel E. Lieberman, published by Pantheon Books.

If you want to be dazzled by the science of the evolution of the human body, and by the role that diet has played in our becoming intelligent humans, then this is a must read. The author is extraordinarily articulate about this subject and always supports his viewpoint with substantive research. He backs every statement with an extensive bibliography. He never loses his firm grip on his viewpoint as an author with knowledge and expertise. Of course, Lieberman recommends exercise and a reasonable diet for the health of a modern person. Very convincing.

Useful Websites:

www.amodernwomansguide.com

You can go to my website to download any journals or forms that I have included in the guide. I will share anything new I learn about food, diet and aging with frequent updates and thoughts.

The United States Department of Agriculture has an official food and diet site. You can find it at: *fnic.nal.usda.gov*.

The government wants to encourage you to be healthy and has created a special website: *www.choosemyplate.gov*. This site includes a food and exercise tracker. You can make your own plan and follow it. Free.

You may be very confused by the plethora of diets. If you want an evaluation of all the different diets around, check out: *www.WebMD.com*.

Do you need help with an eating disorder?

Due to the complexity of food issues in our society, several 12-Step fellowships and a variety of treatment programs have evolved for people suffering from serious eating-related disorders. Perhaps one of these groups or organizations may help you on your search for a healthy relationship with food.

A place to start might be this free service: *www.nationaleatingdisorders.org*

Or you might want to consider Overeaters Anonymous: *www.oa.org*.

How To Use The Food Journal:

This exercise is about mindfulness. There are many ways to consider your consumption of food: calories, fat content, protein intake, sodium levels, raw versus cooked, amount of carbohydrates, and portions. To complete the Guide's journal, there is no need to consult tables, weigh food or control portions. For the next 14 days, simply record and report on what foods you are eating, and how your emotional or sensory life coexists with this activity.

To complete the journal: You may simply list the foods you eat in each section (breakfast, lunch, dinner), check-off the amount of water and alcohol you imbibe, and answer the question of the day for each meal. Use this tool in any manner that seems comfortable, but use it every day for 14 days. You are bringing consciousness to the ordinary experience of feeding your body.

The Food Journal can be downloaded: **www. amodernwomansguide.com**

Reflections on your experience:

When you have completed the full 14 days of journaling then you are ready to reflect on your diet. Are you properly nurturing yourself? How do you feel about the food you eat? How does the food you consume make you feel? Ah, you only completed 9 out of the 14 days. Hmmm, please try again. Just download a new form. You will get more insight into your relationship with food if you consistently and daily work at awareness for the full 14 days.

You have completed your journal and now you are ready to evaluate your experience. Using the journal or any piece of paper write what comes to mind on the subject of *food/eating/dieting.* *Yes, take a pen and paper (or the Guide) and write for 15 minutes (time yourself). Just let it out. No one will ever read what you have to say. Except you. Now read out loud what you have written. Hopefully your handwriting is better than mine. Yes, read it out loud to yourself. Whatever you have say is what you need to hear. Is there anything more you need to express on this subject? Write that down.*

You are ready to consider your relationship to food. Twelve questions:

1. How do you rate your diet?

2. Are you nourishing yourself properly?

3. What foods or drinks trigger off-balance eating?

4. Do you feel that in general you overeat? When and why?

5. What do you really like to eat that you do not allow yourself to have?

6. Do you feel that in general you are eating too little? When and why?

7. What foods make you happy?

8. What could you do to enhance the pleasure of your eating experience?

9. What meal do you enjoy the most?

10. Do you feel that your body is comfortable with the weight you are carrying?

11. Do you know what your body really wants to eat?

12. If you decided to properly nourish yourself what would that look like?

14-day Food Journal

DAY 1 Breakfast	Lunch	Dinner	Snacks	Water Check=8 oz.
				Alcohol 4 oz

Q: How filling was each meal?

A:

DAY 2 Breakfast	Lunch	Dinner	Snacks	Water Check=8 oz.
				Alcohol 4 oz

Q: What were the sounds in the room?

A:

DAY 3 Breakfast	Lunch	Dinner	Snacks	Water Check=8 oz.
				Alcohol 4 oz

Q: What were you thinking about during your meal or snack?

A:

DAY 4 Breakfast	Lunch	Dinner	Snacks	Water Check=8 oz.
				Alcohol 4 oz

Q: Were your meals or snacks healthy?

A:

DAY 5 Breakfast	Lunch	Dinner	Snacks	Water Check=8 oz.
				Alcohol 4 oz

Q: How do you rate your portions– tiny, modest or giant?

A:

DAY 6 Breakfast	Lunch	Dinner	Snacks	Water Check=8 oz.
				Alcohol 4 oz

Q: Rate your level of enjoyment. What was the best food you ate?

A:

DAY 7 Breakfast	Lunch	Dinner	Snacks	Water Check=8 oz.
				Alcohol 4 oz

Q: Where are you? Describe the place, each meal or snack.

A:

DAY 8 Breakfast	Lunch	Dinner	Snacks	Water Check=8 oz.
				Alcohol 4 oz

Q: Time yourself. How long did it take to eat each meal or snack.

A:

DAY 9.Breakfast	Lunch	Dinner	Snacks	Water Check=8 oz.
				Alcohol 4 oz

Q: What kind of mood were you in when you started to eat?

A:

DAY 10 Breakfast	Lunch	Dinner	Snacks	Water Check=8 oz.
				Alcohol 4 oz

Q: How could you have changed this experience?

A:

DAY 11 Breakfast	Lunch	Dinner	Snacks	Water Check=8 oz.
				Alcohol 4 oz

Q: Did this meal or snack make you sad or happy?

A:

DAY 12 Breakfast	Lunch	Dinner	Snacks	Water Check=8 oz.
				Alcohol 4 oz

Q: Did you take second servings or more at each meal or snack?

A:

DAY 13 Breakfast	Lunch	Dinner	Snacks	Water Check=8 oz.
				Alcohol 4 oz

Q: What were the colors of the foods you ate?

DAY 14 Breakfast	Lunch	Dinner	Snacks	Water Check=8 oz.
				Alcohol 4 oz

Q: What would you have changed about the meal or snack?

A:

GEMS OF WISDOM ON LOSING WEIGHT:

You may have decided that you do wish to relinquish a few extra pounds. In the many, many articles and books that I have read about losing weight, certain gems of wisdom show up over and over again. Here is the gold that I gleaned:

Gem Number 1: **Keep a food journal.** Women who write down what they eat and weigh themselves weekly have a much higher success rate in losing weight and keeping it off.

Gem Number 2: **Choose one meal a day that you eat exactly the same food day after day.** People tend to consume more of exciting new foods and less of very ordinary, familiar foods.

Gem Number 3: **Exercise every day.** Exercising early in your day raises your metabolism for the entire day.

Gem Number 4: **Drink lots of water.** If you feel hungry, try drinking some fluid. You may think you are very hungry, but you may just be *thirsty*. Try for 32 ounces of water every day.

Gem Number 5: **Remove "sinful" food from your environment.** Get rid of (throw out or give away) all foods that you have self-labeled unwise or that trigger you to eat out of control. You know what they are. Your partner will be fine. All these foods are readily available outside the home.

Gem Number 6: **Eat fruits and vegetables.** Fresh or frozen vegetables are your allies in weight control and health. Aim for variety and variety in color. Consume a rainbow of fruits and vegetables.

Gem Number 7: **Think quality, not quantity.** This might mean thinking local, thinking organic, and staying away from fast food. *Yes, your food costs may be higher, so select carefully what you eat.*

Gem Number 8: **Eat like a queen.** Savor your food. Set a beautiful table. Make dining a pleasure: sit down, see the food, slowly taste the food. Eat until you are just barely full, not until "I need a nap" or "Why did I eat so much?" full.

Thoughts.......

Thoughts.......

Thoughts.......

Thoughts.......

Chapter Three: Moving Forward

Faraway and long ago, The People roamed the savannah. All thirty of The People spent idyllic spring days living along the ribbon of green next to the river. There were plenty of birds and fish to catch and herbs to gather along the edges of spring streams. After a hard dry season their world was again kind.

Summer was almost here. Soon it would be time to make their annual trek to the seashore where they would consume enormous amounts of shellfish, sea turtles and their large leathery eggs. If The People were blessed, the entire tribe, wading into the sea, would drive the giant, migrating fish into the ready spears. The fish would be dried on the shore with the sacred salt.

The oldest of them was the grandmother whom they called Mai. The tribe depended on her wisdom. She always knew the right moment to leave for the shore, the best plants for fevers, where to dig for roots, and how to find food when times were hard.

This past dry season, more than ever, tiny Mai had shriveled and shrunk. Her skin wrinkled upon wrinkles. Now almost toothless, she still laughed and smiled and hugged all the children.

Mai had been with The People forever. No one living could re-member the time when Mai was not there. This spring she alone had known, when the birthing proved so very difficult, how to help her daughter's daughter deliver a healthy baby girl.

The tribe got ready to leave for the seashore. A simple task, as The People had only minimal possessions, just the few important tools and ritual objects that one individual could carry. They slept in small wood and bark shelters that stayed behind when they moved on. Their dwellings were left for the land to reclaim.

Mai told them this year she could not go with them. She could no longer manage the trek. Even with her walking stick and leaning on her daughter, she could not walk the twenty miles to the shore.

The People were saddened by her decision. Many were frightened. There was no one else in their tribe who remembered as well and as much as Mai. All of them loved her.

The women of the tribe patiently traveled up and down the river searching for a rare plant. Accompanied by the weak but very alert Mai, they identified and collected the special plant called *the long sleep*. The oldest of Mai's daughters was made guardian and keeper of the leaves. She would keep the dried version in a satchel around her neck to use cautiously to relieve pain or in greater amounts to bring death. A generous amount of the fresh herb was given to Mai.

Every member of the tribe was weeping as they moved towards the sea. They looked back for as long as they could—and they could see very far—until the lone stooped figure was lost to them. Mai set quietly by her last fire sipping the herb tea. Now and then, she would lift her thin gnarled hand in a gentle wave of farewell.

Very touching, Claire. And the point is...?

For more than 100,000 years all of us, all *Homo sapiens* lived that life.

We were the hunter-gathers. We walked five miles a day to forage for our tubers, nuts, and greens. We walked for days following a wounded animal whose meat would provide the protein that made our large brains possible. When we could no longer keep up with the tribe, our life was done.

You and I have the same physical characteristics that evolved for a life cycle that is rapidly going extinct.

Instead our modern existence is acutely and dangerously soft and still. We eat too much and do too little.

People stood up on two legs to do one thing well—walk. In fact the shape of our feet (significantly the size of our toes and the position of our big toe), our center of gravity and our leg muscles make us unique primates. Both men and women can walk for long distances.

Human babies are born with large soft heads, totally helpless. Human babies are essentially born prematurely. If the infant remained in the womb long enough to allow the head to become bigger, then the mother's hip structure would have to enlarge to allow the passage of the head. Women who could birth a more developed infant would be unable to walk and run. The trade-off for women's capacity for long distance movement is a difficult and dangerous birthing process. Dangerous for both the mother and her child—one or both of them could die.

This is important. Your body still thinks you belong to a hunter-gatherer designed to move until you die.

And think about this. You are mistaken if you think that early human populations did not have elders. It is true that many of the babies, many of the young children, and many of the childbearing women died. However, if the rare woman did survive to be 40 years old, she could expect to live another 17 to 24 more years.

Old women in primitive societies escaped walkers, wheelchairs, oxygen, feeding tubes, diapers, and the indignity of life beyond functioning and purpose.

They kept moving until the end.

When you were a baby, a small girl, an adolescent, a busy adult, you moved and danced and squirmed and jumped for joy (when is the last time you did that?) and had a hard time sitting down.

These days, as you become an older woman, you may just want to sit on the couch in the sun reading the *New Yorker*. Or you may be very fit—playing tennis, skiing and hiking. Or somewhere in-between.

As we age, we all slow down. If you were a hyperactive adult, your slackening might be a relief for friends and family. If you were an "I will get it done it my own time" relaxed type, you might be in acute slow motion and not even be aware of it.

Most of us are participating in modern, technological society. With every new time and motion saving device developed, you and I end up farther and farther from a lifestyle that is true to our natural design. We are imprisoning our bodies in a stagnant and sedentary lifestyle.

No, we are not (as long as civilization stands) going to abandon our automobiles, our washing machines, dishwashers, our entertainment centers, our computers, our vacuum cleaners or our smart phones. Nor would I want to.

Quite the dilemma for the modern women as the years goes by. If you and I are on a crusade to age well, our origins give us interesting clues.

We will have to strengthen our cardiovascular system, encourage our muscles, and improve our flexibility and balance. Indeed, we need to toughen up, as if the savannah were still our home.

If our modern lifestyle is artificial and indeed bad for us, then we have to deliberately compensate for what is lacking in our culture. If we want to grow old with grace, stay mobile, strong, healthy, and mentally alert, we will have to make exercise an important part of our daily life.

You may decide that it is time to relax and just do whatever you damn well feel like doing. Fair enough. **Warning:** As we age, we are losing muscle mass, and our bones are getting fragile. Without our being aware of it, our balance and strength are both gradually lessening. What if when you least want it or expect it, you fall and break your hip? It is a long way up.

All my research on the topic of dealing with aging distills to exercise, exercise, and exercise. This is definitely an "all roads lead to the gym" conclusion. So, if you are certain you have already implemented the perfect fitness plan for yourself, or are sure you do not want to have this information, please skip this chapter.

Well, it won't hurt you to at least read it.

MOVE IT OR LOSE IT

How fit do you think you are?

It has been a long time since I lived in a city and ran, cursing and desperate to get to class on time, after the midtown bus. The public bus, that just as I got to its yellow doors, slammed them shut and maliciously drove off. Would that dash for a bus give me a heart attack today? Have I allowed my cardiovascular system to weaken so much that I cannot take physical or mental stress without causing a heart attack or stroke?

Often, what we think of as the symptoms of aging are the results of our bodies weakening and becoming less fit.

We have to be purposeful and focused to make our bodies move enough to keep vital, and we have to be very, very conscious to keep our body tuned- up and engaged.

Eight reasons to make exercise part of your life:

1. Exercise can be as effective as taking drugs for heart disease and high blood pressure.

2. Exercise will affect the very engine of your cells. Those fabulous mitochondria bacteria energy-makers in your cells will increase and perform better.

3. Exercise will make you feel happier. Exercise is a mood elevator and vigorous exercise is a terrific attitude changer.

4. Exercise stimulates your immune system, which lowers the risk of some cancers, reduces arthritic symptoms and helps your body heal.

5. Exercise helps maintain a healthy weight by improving your use of glucose. It thereby lowers your risk of getting—or helps you to control—Type 2 Diabetes.

6. Exercise helps to maintain healthy bones, muscles and joints.

7. Exercise lowers your risk of falling, and of injuring yourself, if you do fall.

8. You will look better.

Two more great reasons to exercise:

1. After the initial effort, you will have a great deal more energy.

2. Your brain will work faster, better and for a longer time.

When thinking about creating your own exercise plan, consider why, when, where, how, how much, and who is in charge. One of your goals is to increase your general level of activity and just move your body more during daily life.

You may be asking yourself, " How much exercise is enough to make me feel youthful? What exactly would be the best plan to conserve my strength and mobility?" Or even, "What could I do to become super fit?"

Meet four wonderful ladies—real dolls. They have been created to provide models of behavior so any resemblance to your friends is purely coincidental.

Lynda, Marianne, Gail and Barbra are four women all born in 1950. Each was born in a different part of the country. They met as college students at an Eastern liberal arts college in the late 60s. The four of them majored in men, drugs, rock 'n' roll, and English Literature. All four graduated in June of 1972.

Now they are senior citizens leading very different lives. The four friends still stay in touch, and two years ago met for a long cheerful weekend in Marianne's hometown, Austin, Texas.

90

Lynda, a retired magazine editor, blue-eyed and beautiful, can still wear her jeans from her college days. L. still lives in the East, is divorced and remarried. Her second marriage is to Bob, the guy who took her to the high school prom. They found each other again at their 30th high school reunion that neither was quite certain they wanted to attend. Lynda was athletic in her youth and a cheerleader in high school. Today she rarely exercises except for an occasional round of golf, or a doubles tennis match. She is not serious about fitness and counts on her youthful athleticism when she wants to play at sports. L. has pretty firm breasts and truly a lovely figure. She keeps her weight down by drinking one cup of black coffee for breakfast and always having salad for lunch. Lynda enjoys her evenings with Bob. Their dinner is always preceded by a "happy hour" of wine or cocktails. Lynda consumes most of her daily calories at dinner.

Marianne is from the Midwest, now living in Texas. Marianne, a lawyer, runs the homeless advocacy program for her chosen city. M. has always struggled with her weight and never considered herself at all athletic. However, after reading about the benefits of exercise, she adopted Chester, a young active dog, from the animal shelter. Every day she and Chester walk two miles in the local park. Occasionally, she takes a yoga class or a Zumba class with her new partner Susan. Marianne has moved on from her marriage to "cheating Tom", and is enjoying trying new activities with Susan.

Gail, originally from Seattle, now living in Vermont, is still married to the "younger man"—the handsome doctor Steve that she met in the Peace Corps. Gail went to medical school after the birth of her twins and is now a doctor specializing in urology. One year ago, after extensive reading on the subject, G. dedicated herself to a comprehensive exercise program. She does weight training twice a week, yoga twice a week, and a cardio program that makes her really sweat four times a week. Steve is amazed at Gail's new energy and has started his own fitness program.

Barbra, a retired movie producer still living in Southern California, has always been competitive. B. was a state champion track star in high school. She has always kept very fit. Two years ago, Barbara started participating in triathlons. She is a serious athlete and committed to her training program. B. swims an hour a day, bicycles about 100 miles a week, and runs five miles every other day. She also has a trainer who works on strengthening her legs. Recently she sprained her ankle, but after two days of rest she is back at it. Barbra is training for the Hawaiian Iron Man Competition and expects to win. B. was widowed ten years ago. When interested in sex, she chooses athletic fit men, preferably not actors. Barbra has no time for romance, nor does she want a long-term partner.

Do you identify with any of these women?

Who do you think has the best chance of remaining youthful and vital?

Let us ask Sage Moon (an imaginary but true-to-type) Hollywood fitness guru to assess the lifestyles of the four friends.

Sage Moon considers the lovely, blue-eyed Lynda.

Of course, Lynda looks terrific always, but although her weight has not changed since high school, her body composition has. We all lose muscle mass as we age. Her ratio of body fat to muscle has dramatically increased. Lynda is thin on the outside and fat on the inside.

L. could well afford to gain healthy weight as her Body Mass Index which is below 18.5 puts her at risk. Lynda would benefit from doing *any* form of exercise regularly. Her occasional fits of intense activity are actually dangerous as she is much weaker and in worse cardiovascular shape than she knows. Sage's advice to Lynda: "Eat breakfast every morning, exercise regularly, and limit yourself to three ounces of alcohol a day."

Next Sage Moon contemplates the somewhat round Marianne.

Marianne, who has a BMI of 31 but has kept a trim waistline, has a lower mortality risk than Lynda, especially since she regularly walks more than 30 minutes a day. Sage Moon feels that Marianne could use strength training twice a week to increase her muscle mass, but that M. is definitely moving in the right direction if she wants to live well to the end of her days.

Sage Moon smiles to think of Gail and her threefold exercise approach to fitness. "Gail has the perfect exercise program."

Gail's program includes strength training, regular cardio work, and attention to balance and flexibility. If G. stays with her program as the years roll by, she has the *best* chance of the four friends to remain active, attractive and alert.

Sage Moon shakes her head and sighs when considering the fitness of the extreme athlete Barbara.

Barbra's desire to win, and her disciplined approach to being an athlete are important tools to give her a sense of purpose. However, Barbra's immune system may be weakened by the stress of her intense regime. Her hard and frequent workouts make her vulnerable to injury. The huge amount she exercises actually has no more health benefit than the comprehensive program Gail follows. In this case Sage Moon cautions, "Less may be more."

And you? How do you want to approach your own exercise program? To aid you in constructing your own path to vitality, I have included some suggestions at the end of the chapter. But first, let's define exercise.

**Exercise is motion with focused mental concentration
and physical intensity for a specific duration.**

A group of women who worked as hotel maids became the subjects of a well-funded research project on the psychology of exercise. This was a Harvard study engaging 88 maids from seven hotels. Two domestic workers, Rita and Maria, agreed to measure how their long days of changing bed linens and scrubbing bathrooms affected their fitness levels. The women were divided into two groups, Rita in one and Maria in another.

Rita and her group were simply told to continue their usual activities as hotel workers. However, Maria and her group were informed that their chores qualified as aerobic exercises and had weight-loss benefits.

After six weeks, the Rita group showed no improvement in fitness levels nor did they lose any weight. But, *hello!* The Maria ladies (remember: they were told their chores were exercise) lost weight and showed marked improvement in their fitness levels.

Mental intention or focus is more important than most women appreciate and is the "secret" ingredient in succeeding at any athletic endeavor or fitness plan.

Time for a toothy quote from the Scientific American August 2013 issue: "Most people do not realize that sustained bouts of moderate to vigorous physical activities changes our bodies from the inside out, starting with the neural connections in the brain and extending all the way out to major muscles and bones of the limb."

When can I consider my activities exercise? Is walking the dog exercise? Dancing to Tina Turner? Is cleaning the house exercise? Is sex exercise? Yes—to all of them. And especially when your mind considers the activity to have fitness benefits.

Any form of movement that gets you off the couch or from behind the desk on a regular basis will lower your mortality risk.

How do I know if I am exercising strenuously enough to change my body?

Some of our activities provide physical stimulus, but could be considered light exercise. Light exercise will keep us in shape but not create a major change in our physical condition. Taking a leisurely stroll around the park with my dog is light activity level. I could easily (without an extra puff of air) shout, "Rover, come. Good boy. Now, sit. Very good boy!" I wish my body were as obedient as my dog.

Moderate exercise includes activities that take some effort and are sustained for more time. For me, moderate exercise might be a three-mile walk on a mountain country road with a final sprint at the end to get home to the bathroom. My heart is pounding, but I can still talk.

Vigorous exercise demands consistent attention and effort. Sweat (not light lady-like perspiration) is the signal you are exerting yourself enough.

Here is a definition of taking it to the limit: You can barely talk, and you need to concentrate to formulate the words: "Yes, I am working hard, and I am loving it."

Real change in the body requires the stimulus of activities that raise your heart level, make you sweat, and push your body beyond your comfort level.

To get results, you and I will need to exercise at this level for **30** minutes, **four** times a week.

My daughter, Vanessa, was a soccer player, skier, and mountain bike fiend. She tells me my generation of women is not athletic and never really learned to physically "work-at-it."

I agree that my city "gym" class emphasized attitude over any athletic endeavor. My teacher graded her students on how we looked, not how we performed. It was considered important to have a neatly ironed and creased gym uniform. Ha, I still do not know how to wield an iron. I barely passed my gym class.

I have had to learn to be a modern athletic woman (post Title IX— the federal ruling that gave us equal time on the sport field). I have learned to "push" myself beyond what I used to think was enough exertion. When working out, I feel triumphant when I have to brush the rivulets of sweat from my eyes.

What kind of shape are you in? Fair, good, excellent—you may not be in as good a shape as you might think. Or surprise, surprise—you may be in much better condition than you thought. Do you want to consult your physician? This could be a good idea, especially if you have been ignoring your body for years. Does running to answer the phone, carrying heavy packages, or walking briskly make you breathe heavily or begin to sweat? These are warning signs that your cardiovascular system is being compromised.

I will say it again loud and clear: if you want to stay youthful for as long as possible, you are going to have to create high-intensity, sweaty (i.e.: aerobic) opportunities at least four times a week.

In addition, you will need to encourage yourself to move more often in the pattern of your daily life. Take the stairs instead the elevator;

park the car away from the entrance. Take time to walk instead of ride. Play the music that rocked your boat at twenty. Turn up the music and dance. Move those legs. Shake that booty. Smile. Begin to find the joy and make friends with your precious aging body.

Yes, this might be a lifestyle change.

You: "I am in such terrible shape I do not remember when I walked anywhere, danced, bicycled or swam. What can I do?" See your doctor for an evaluation of your health. If you are not at grave risk for a heart attack, but really in poor physical shape, then begin slowly.

You may set a goal that you cannot immediately reach. Work steadily towards improving your physical condition. Considering our biological clock, you and I needed to commit to action five years and two months ago. Procrastination is not your best choice.

BE AWARE OF YOUR BODY. KNOW WHEN TO STOP. PAY ATTENTION TO YOURSELF. REST IS BEST IF YOU ARE EXHAUSTED. THERE IS BALANCE IN EVERYTHING.

Reminder: More woman die of heart attacks then men. You are trying to prevent a heart attack not *cause* one. Know the warning signs of heart attack, the number one killer of elderly woman:

1. Uncomfortable pressure, squeezing, fullness or pain in the center of your chest.

2. Pain or discomfort in one or both arms, the back, neck, jaw or stomach.

3.. Shortness of breath, with or without chest discomfort.

4. Other signs such as breaking out in a cold sweat, nausea, exhaustion, or lightheadedness.

5. Women's most common heart attack symptom is chest pain.

But women are more likely than men to experience some of the other symptoms, particularly shortness of breath, nausea/vomiting, extreme paleness, and back or jaw pain. If you feel unusual and terrible, do not take any chances. Trust yourself. You may be having a heart attack.

The medical community has ignored many women in the midst of cardiac failure. Often female symptoms do not fit the standard profile of a man having a heart attack.

If you have any suspicions you are in trouble, insist upon getting medical attention. When you do get medical attention, insist you be thoroughly examined for a heart attack.

If you have any of these signs, don't wait more than five minutes before calling for help. Call 911 and get to a hospital right away.

You might save a friend or yourself. Know the warning signs of a stroke:

1. Sudden numbness or weakness of face, arm or leg—especially on one side of the body;

2. Sudden confusion, trouble speaking or understanding;

3. Sudden trouble seeing in one or both eyes;

4. Sudden trouble walking, dizziness, loss of balance or coordination;

5. Sudden severe headache with no known cause.

You may be in trouble if you cannot raise both arms or smile or speak a simple sentence, as in, "I am feeling perfectly fine. Why are you wearing those awful pink sweatpants?"

Exercise safely. But I have been encouraging you to exercise vigorously, and to sweat profusely! Am I trying to kill you? Absolutely not. You and I are mature women, in charge of our bodies, finding a pathway to stay vital. *Always listen to what your body has to say and respect the information.*

Let us continue to look at the important ways we can maintain our physical *joie de vivre.*

Consider becoming a pious student of yoga, Pilates, tai chi, or qigong, because these practices ask for physical and mental effort while providing benefits. These include stress reduction, increased flexibility and balance, improved posture, as well as some strength and aerobic benefits. Yoga and tai chi have been around for centuries. These wise, ancient systems emphasize the role of the mind in engaging the body and maximizing your effort.

And if you want to amaze yourself with your own vitality and strength, then consider weight or resistance training. In 2001, I asked a gerontologist, a doctor specialized in working with the elderly, if she could name one thing that would help most in stalling the aging process. She said, "Weight or resistance training." Of course, it took me ten years to apply the information to myself. **The elderly, more than any age group, respond to weight training and gain muscle mass at a higher rate than younger participants.**

Many women of my generation have a queasy image of weight training. Your visual may include bronzed, greased up, and oddly rippled men or women grimacing in strange, rather unattractive poses. The strength or resistance training I am so eager for you to try will not have any effect that will make you resemble Arnold Schwarzenegger in his prime. The correct strength training will make you look smaller, stand taller, enjoy sex more, make it easier for you to lose weight, and feel more like dancing.

For the readers of this guide who might suspect me of overstating the virtues of weight training or even speciously making it up, let me introduce you to Walter Frontera, M.D., William Evans, Ph.D. and Maria Fiatarone, M.D., of the Tufts Center on Aging. I was delighted when I located these researchers who provided important studies on the effects on strength training on aging in both the young old and the frail elderly.

Several important studies changed everyone's opinion of weight training. I will summarize them for you here.

The first group of 60 to 70-year old men were supervised and exercised at 80 percent of capacity. In just 12 weeks, the men's strength increased from 100 to 175 percent.

The second group of six women and four men were weak, frail elderly folks living in a nursing home. They ranged in age from 86 to 96. The director of the home had to be convinced, but he allowed the study. Three times a week, for eight weeks, they followed a genuine weight lifting program lifting weights at 80 percent of capacity. After eight weeks *(drum roll)*, the old ones increased their strength by an average of 175 percent. This made a big difference. Two participants were so much stronger that they abandoned their canes.

The third group, a study of women ages 50 to 70 years conducted at the Jean Mayer Research Center on Aging at Tufts University in 1993 and 1994, also showed dramatic results. There was nothing subtle about the major improvements to the health of the woman who participated.

This study of older women, designed by Miriam E. Nelson, Ph.D., is truly inspirational. What did it do for the participants? After one year of training, their bodies tested younger than the year before.

Strength training did many great things for these women's bodies:

1. It halted bone loss.

2. It increased activity levels.

3. It increased muscle mass and strength.

4. It increased the women's sense of well being and confidence.

Money matters. Considering the limited economic resources of many senior women, how much money are you ready to commit to your exercise program? What can you realistically spend? Can you make this a bigger priority than some other activity that may not be as beneficial?

What can you do at home or in the neighborhood? If you can afford it, I would recommend you join a health club, a local pool, or a local recreation center. If you are already a member of a facility, can you make better use of your membership?

Need information? Need help? Research it. Google it. Ask around. What is close by? Does your insurance cover any program? What facility seems the friendliest, the most cost effective, or has great instructors? You choose.

Remember you are in charge of your body. Yes, you are the captain of the team and the head cheerleader. If you have the funds, I would recommend a trainer, at least to get you started. She or he will make you work harder than you would on your own, will help you understand gym equipment, and perhaps design a program you can do on your own.

WHERE IS THE JOY?

You will need to experiment. Even if you are committed to exercise, you still will be more likely to show up if you enjoy the activity.

FIND THE PLEASURE.

Swim, run, play basketball or tennis, belly dance, ice skate, bike, practice martial arts, row, pole dance, exercise to CDs, fast walk with weights, or just plain walk. What did you like to do as a child? You may take this sport or activity up again. You can view looking for the right exercise plan as an adventure, a game, and a time to explore new sensations. This can be a time to renew parts of your self that have been missing for decades.   You may be getting older, but you do not have to act like an old fogey.

Here it is one more time: To be a vital senior, a realistic goal would be to exercise at an intense level for a 30-minute session four times a week, with some form of weight training twice a week, and at least once a week to take a more meditative class in a discipline such as yoga.

Letting go of resistance, letting go of fixed ideas about what you will try, and letting go of a negative attitude will make the process of solving your exercise puzzle much more effective. *Imagine change.*

PLAN TO EXERCISE.

WORK YOUR PLAN.

Continuing the Conversation

Suggested Readings:

Strong Women Stay Young written by Miriam E. Nelson, Ph.D, with Sara Wernich, Ph.D., published by Bantam Books.

This gung-ho book stresses the value of strength training. You may be converted. The authors were part of the research team that proved the hypothesis that weight training has many benefits. *Strong Women Stay Young* is designed to help you begin and adhere to a strength-training program. It is an excellent well-organized tool. There are helpful exercises and charts. This book is a keeper. As a senior woman, you will feel included and appreciated. Our specific issues are addressed. You may be inspired to begin a weight- training program. However, if your budget allows, I strongly recommend you engage the services of a professional *trainer, at least to begin your program.*

Younger Next Year for Women written by Chris Crowley & Henry S. Lodge M.D., published by Workman Publishing.

This is a lively and loud book about the value of exercise. The authors are two men with *all the answers.* The two male voices make me feel I am listening to: one, a caring, but stern father (Chris) or two, a tough older brother (Henry). You might like the tone of the book. Or not. Here is one gem of wisdom from the book: "Do not go on a diet, but quit eating crap." A triumph of language. This book may convince you to do more cardio exercise. I am convinced, now guys, stop twisting my arm.

Yoga from the Inside Out written by Christina Sell, published by Hohm Press.

This is a soft and sweet-talking book that gently conceals a radical feminist viewpoint. Throughout the volume, we are treated to photographs of women with ordinary figures. I recognized myself. This book talks a great deal about respecting and listening to our bodies. _Great advice._ This is very positive book emphasizing self-acceptance and the cultivation of our higher self.

Useful Websites:

www.amodernwomansguide.com

You can go to my website to download any journals or forms that I have included in the guide. I will share anything new I learn about exercise, fitness and aging with frequent updates and thoughts.

For some sensible advice and inspiration try:

www.shapefit.com

Or read about fitness and health at: _www.webmd.com_

If you need or want to work out at home, you may consult this site for recommendations on exercise videos: _www.videofitness.com_

Finding fitness:

Looking for the right match:

You have gone to your doctor and gotten the green light. Now you are ready to begin. You are ready to become fit. Even eager. However, you are unsure how to find the right format to become *strong and vital*. A good way to locate exercise options is to consult the yellow pages or the internet.

We are friends (in the literary sense), but I do not know where you live. I randomly decided to be helpful to my readers in Des Moines, Iowa. I researched the exercise world in Des Moines; I was astonished at the rich and varied menu of fitness choices.

I found 98 listings for health clubs and fitness centers. These were facilities where I could take care of both my strength training and my cardio fitness needs. If I lived in Des Moines, I would probably begin with the clubs nearest my home. I found that I could try out most of these facilities for free. The clubs offered me anywhere from a one-day to a three-day pass. *No charge.* Come as our guest. How nice.

You and I have learned that to have the "perfect" exercise program, we need to become friendly with the three graces—*strength, cardio-fitness, and flexibility*. I decided that the health clubs and fitness centers could not meet all my needs. What about independent yoga and Pilates studios? There were dozens of locations that I could visit to concentrate on flexibility and balance. I emailed them: "I am a senior citizen looking for the yoga studio/ Pilates studio/tai chi center/Qigong institute that is right for me—do you offer a one-time trial class?" Guess what? They all said they would be delighted to allow me to try a class—no charge. More free experiences. Thank you.

In Des Moines, Iowa, I could get fit just by taking advantage of all the free-trial passes. Chuckle. Sooner rather than later, I would choose a place with a great pool, that was very clean, and that had a friendly staff. I would join my blue-ribbon winner. I would set up a weekly schedule, and I would commit to my program. Intention, action and discipline. I would hope my first-choice gym/club would be convenient to my work or my home. And I might really bond with one of the Pilates or yoga instructors and attend as many of his or her classes as possible.

Some folks do not like gyms and certainly, there are other helpful alternatives: the great outdoors, dance studios, ice skating rinks, horseback riding stables, You-Tube, DVDs, or just anything you will do regularly that will keep you moving. The focus is simply to keep your body going strong. With some persistence and a lack of resistance, yes, you can find your way to include exercise in your life.

FINDING TIME FOR FITNESS WILL GIVE YOU MORE
ALIVE TIME.

Thoughts.......

Thoughts.......

110

Thoughts......

Thoughts.......

Thoughts.…...

Thoughts.......

Chapter Four: Together We Search for Meaning and Purpose

Women and men are unusual animals. *Homo sapiens* means the wise or knowing man. We are aware of self, conscious of being alive. We may not want to talk about it, but one of the gifts of our mindfulness is the knowing of our own eventual death.

We are thoughtful women. As a group let us give ourselves a new designation: *Femina sapiens*, the wise women. We have the capacity to learn and change throughout our entire lifetimes. You and I can develop new habits and expand our consciousness at any age.

Women have big heads—and, of course, so do men. What I mean by this is that the proportional size of our brains to our body weight, compared to any mammal the same size, is the largest of any living being. This relationship is called the index of cephalization. Ah, the poetry of science. We also have a beautiful cerebral cortex, complex brain folds, and an enormous quantity of neurons. Huh! Read it again.

Yes, women are very intelligent. Our hungry heads require 20 percent of our daily calorie intake and rule our lives from birth to death. Our brain is a mysterious and special organ. Because we are such brain-dominated primates, it is a given that how we think or feel will affect our health and our longevity. Our intellect and the human talent of self-awareness permit us to choose how we envision our reality, and give us the potential to change our environment and alter our life path.

As clever and capable as we became, you and I, we were born weak, dependent and speechless. We were babies unable to lift our large awkward heads. As infants and throughout our extended childhoods, we needed devotion and care to survive. We matured into adults slowly and sometimes with great difficulty. Many of us have enjoyed a successful and productive adulthood. Some of us have already experienced and survived grave illness and/or traumatic crises. Some of us will age gently. Some of us will die as weak, dependent and helpless as we came into life. Like our infant self, barely able to lift our heads.

Yes, you and I, we are getting older, and we are much closer to our exit than our arrival on earth. *How do you feel? Do you feel frightened, angry, or cheated? Are you mourning the loss of youth? What happened to my figure? Why didn't I go back to school and become a_____? Why did I divorce my first husband? Why didn't I own my sexuality? Why didn't I have or adopt a child? Why didn't I claim my power?*

Or you may have few regrets. You may feel pleased with how your life has unfolded. As you grow older, you are much less constricted by the rules that were internalized from your interactions with parents, society, and/or religion. As time passes, do you feel freer and more contented and more accepting of yourself? Hurrah!

You may be quite willing to age naturally. You may feel dignified and secure in your own evolving. You might feel your body getting older is like the seasons' progression and feel comfortable even cozy in the winter of your life. You may be looking forward to life after death.

Some spiritual beliefs offer the faithful the certainty of continuance after the end of the body. For many women, religion and religious organizations offer emotional and social sanctuary. Your belief system may make you confident that as a unique identity, you will endure forever in some form. Myself, I cannot be certain. For one, I cannot imagine a higher being who judges me. Nor a punishing God, who cares if I eat pork, show my face in public, make love to another woman, or choose to have an abortion. I may be in big trouble.

I do know that matter can transform, but is never lost. When we die, our physical body will break down. After our brain and heart fail, and we expire, our body will eventually disintegrate into atoms, neutrons and subatomic particles. We reunite with the universal energy field. This is where physics meets philosophy. You may be joyfully practicing Buddhism, reciting prayers from the Torah, or singing in a Gospel choir. I am moved by the interconnectedness of the universe.

You and I, as older women, may or may not agree about religion or if there is life after death. As modern women, can we agree that we want life in life—aging body or no? Can we agree that a mindful here and now is something we both seek? **Can we agree to respect our different personal viewpoints?**

Like me, you are a complicated and individual person. The focus and life choices that you make as a no longer young woman will profoundly affect your health and your resilience. In the beginning of this guide, I offered a concise and rather stern chapter on the common indicators of aging. Chapters Two and Three are practical discussions on coping with and challenging our mature bodies. I hope that I have communicated some very specific options we have for tending to our senior physiques. I am thrilled to know how to take care of the definitely getting older Claire. I am working on keeping my body as youthful as I can for as long as possible. I believe that my action and discipline are positively working to enhance my life and experience.

However...

This chapter attempts to deal with the more psychological and social influences that will affect your personal aging process. This is a discussion about how we feel about our lives. Simply accepting growing old and enjoying the moment is certainly one way of coping with the unfolding season. However, you might want to consider how you wish to use your remaining time. Making positive and innovative changes in how you are spending your last energies may make a difference in the meaning of your entire life. We are modern woman. Traditional female roles that your mother or grandmother sustained may not work for you. You may want to rewrite the script and you can.

How you treat your body and what you eat may matter less than your mindset. Some of the influences that will determine how well and long you live include diverse factors such as: being an ethical person, paying conscientious attention to obligations, cultivating your intimate partnerships, being actively engaged in a community, or committing deeply to your work.

Dear Reader, I can hear you now. I can imagine you confronting me:

"Claire, I cannot believe this. After all you have said about taking care of my corporal body, now you are saying that it may not make a difference. I have just paid for two months of physical training, thrown out all the Godiva chocolate, and bought two new workout outfits."

Keep doing what you are doing.

Think of yourself as an expensive vintage automobile that needs loving care and attention, not to mention waxing and polishing. It is fantastic that you are paying attention to your body and diet, because this will also transform your energy and your attitude. The work you are doing to optimize your physical health will change how you manage the rest of your presence on earth. I sincerely believe that exercise and diet do make a difference in the quality and length of your lifespan.

Now that you have put in place and are practicing your well-designed strategy for taking care of your body, let us contemplate some of the environmental and psychological factors that, according to the statisticians, influence longevity:

- Education (the higher the level, the longer the life)

- Money (prosperity adds years)

- Status (being the boss is better than being middle management)

- Marriage (especially if you're a man)

- Especially marriage to Jesus (being a nun): American Catholic nuns are 27 percent more likely to live into their 70s than other woman.

- Winning the Nobel Peace Prize

- Living in Minnesota

These are all real dynamics that seem to increase life expectancy. Shall we all become nuns and move to Minnesota? Only if you truly love Jesus and ice fishing.

Today: Are you proud of your choices and accomplishments? Do you have dear friends as well as interesting enemies? Have you misbehaved and are afraid you will be reborn as a rat? Do you have a life purpose?

Here's an old-fashioned question for you: *"Are you happy?"*

Happy. A word that slinks along, "happy" fits well with other cloying adjectives like nice, sweet, quiet, well behaved, clean, neat, and chaste. The language that makes up a rulebook for an old-fashioned girl—weak, de-sexed, codependent and underpaid. Is this how we want to be defined as older women? I, Claire, want to be a powerful woman with life focus and vitality. *What about you?*

Do happy old people live longer? It seems they do. If we want to put happiness on our list of "what to do to stay healthy", how do we define our own idea of contentment? How do we achieve a state of personal fulfillment? Will we know when we get there?

And human beings seem to need other human beings. Most people (but not all) are better off spending time with and being close to other people. Our ancestors lived in interdependent clans or tribes. Survival hinged on cooperation. Antisocial behavior could threaten the tribe and result in the isolation of the offending person. Being shunned by the members of your tribe was a terrible punishment for any wrong doing. Being exiled from the group was certain death. Early human beings were with their kinfolk from birth through all life experiences. Do you have a tribe? Do you need a clan? **Community connection affects our health and our longevity.** Choosing a lifestyle that incorporates some form of community will keep you alive longer than your lonely neighbor.

How does this work? Let us visit mid-20th century, Roseto, Pennsylvania, USA, named for the Italian village of Roseto Valfortore. Italian men with mining skills arrived to work the valuable stone quarries of Pennsylvania. The men brought their extended families from the old country to the new town in America. Both Roseto, Italy, and Roseto, USA, in the mid-20th century had a traditional lifestyle of a close-knit society. Life in Roseto, USA, was simple and well defined. The men went to the quarries. The women stayed home and made pasta. The elderly were welcome and honored in the family home. The children obeyed the adults.

Even the dogs knew their place. If you walked down the street you knew everyone and greeted everyone in Italian. *Buongiorno Senora. Buongiorno.*

If it was Tuesday, you as the woman of the household had just made fresh ravioli and sausage. On Thursday, you and your family ate pasta and meatballs just like the other families all over town. Really. Of course on Sunday, everyone was shined up and could be found sitting in a pew at Our Lady of Mount Carmel, heads bowed, listening to the Father say Mass. Hail Mary, full of grace.

You knew what ceremonies would be performed for all life's important moments. You knew when you died just what would be said for you, done for you, where you would be buried, and often who would be your neighbor in the cemetery. Yes, this was a specific and very tightly patterned way of life.

Was everybody happy? Happy or not, they were living long lives. Researchers from neighboring universities discovered Roseto, and from 1934 to 1985 they thoroughly studied the population. Roseto was a community without serious crime and with very low death rates from any form of illness, including cancer and heart disease. Scientists named this phenomenon "The Roseto Effect". People just a few miles away died younger and sicker. The eventual consensus was that the social or clan aspect of this town kept people healthier and alive longer.

Sorry, fans of the Mediterranean Diet. This working-class community could not afford to purchase imported olive oil, so their food was cooked with the much cheaper lard. Community support provided more significant health benefits than dietary choices, work, or lifestyle.

Today Roseto, Pennsylvania is just like Anywhere, USA. As the next generations became regular, upwardly mobile Americans, they began to die just like regular Americans.

Can we learn how to live longer more fulfilled lives from studying traditional societies? Do you *want* to partake in a rigidly delineated community with a very traditional role assigned to you as an aging woman? Is this your idea of bliss?

Modern women take on many identities as we travel from child to senior citizen. My roles in a long life have included student, grocery clerk, secretary (awful as I could not type), waitress, actress (surprisingly talented), wife, mother, business owner, artist, jewelry designer (finally, I earn a decent wage) and grandmother. How many costumes have you worn?

How close are you to your family—mother, father, siblings, aunts, uncles or cousins? As an older woman, you may have outlasted the cast of characters from your childhood. Do you have children, nieces, nephews, godchildren or grandchildren? How cozy are you with this younger generation? How traditional has your role as a woman been? Have you ever been the *stay-at-home-in-the-kitchen-ironing-the-shirts* woman?

As for myself, I spent years at home caring for my two little girls and making sure my husband had clean shirts to wear to the office. I took my homemaker role seriously. Early in my married life I learned to make excellent lasagna that I still serve at family gatherings.

The first time I attempted to cook lasagna, I had to take two buses to shop in the historic Italian neighborhood. The handsome wavy-haired man at the counter welcomed me with a smile. Of course, then I was young and quite voluptuous. I purchased the special cheeses, fresh stored-in-water mozzarella (scamorza), aged Parmigiano Reggiano, and creamy ricotta. I bought the best olive oil from the old country. I splurged on a heavy expensive lasagna pan that I still use forty years later. I carefully transported all the weighty bags onto the two buses it took to get home, trudged with my burdens the four city blocks to my building, walked up the two flights of stairs and through my long narrow apartment and finally into my kitchen.

I was determined to do it right. I made—from scratch—Marinara sauce. I sliced the moist slippery cheeses, flavored the ricotta with hand-ground nutmeg. I boiled pots and pots of water for the long awkward strips of pasta. I carefully layered the olive oiled pan with my homemade sauce, the cheeses and pasta, and sprinkled the dish with finely chopped fresh parsley and basil. I felt at one with the hard-working women of the world.

I was in the kitchen for days. Well, maybe six hours.

I had made a very delicious dish for friends and family. I served this dish and 30 minutes later it was all gone.... The best lasagna I ever made. One of the biggest culinary successes of my life. It took effort, but it was an edible symbol of my affection for family and friends. I still make lasagna in my old pan. Honestly, I take a few shortcuts now, but it is quite

126

delicious. Ask my grandchildren. My personal recipe for this savory dish is at the end of the chapter. The secret is to use the best ingredients you can find and cook with love.

Yes, I truly love my family. Yet, as I age, the focus of my day is not the caring and nurturing of my immediate family. In many ways the ending of this intimate cycle is a loss, and in many ways it is a relief. I no longer make dinner for a hungry husband and young daughters. Most nights alone, I just eat something careless and quick.

The point is: I cannot return to the past. I am a widow. My children are grown individuals whose ways often puzzle me. My grandchildren are being parented differently than I brought up my girls, whom I definitely mothered in a different way than I was raised. If I moved into one of my daughter's home, she would not know what to do with me. "Mom, you are a very messy cook." She would not like me in her kitchen. I would be grumpy and uncomfortable. I believe this is true.

You may live next door to your son and his family. You may interact with your grandchildren every day. In the best human tradition, you are vital to the children's growth and development. You are appreciated and cherished. You are an important part of the clan, still in the bosom of an intact family life.

However, like me, you are a woman living in the 21st century. Many of us do not expect to or may not want to live out an old-style role. If we are not living out a traditional life pattern, then what will be the focus of this very important and final part of our existence?

How can we design a new mythos for our time and our aging? I am defining mythos as a pattern of beliefs and attitudes that have signification, truth or meaning for a culture. Let us choose or invent a vibrant, enlightened story for our last years.

Some of my readers may have very few choices. Your hearts and hands may still be bound tightly by duties of caretaking. You might have a mother who is quite old and has dementia, a partner whose health is degenerating, or an adult child who suddenly needs you again. And millions of grandmothers are raising their children's children, for many reasons, most of them very sad.

If this describes your situation, please consider joining a support group. Group backup is vital for caregivers. Try to locate one in your area. Or search the Internet as a way to connect. My husband was ill for most of our marriage. The toll on my psyche and wellbeing was enormous. I acknowledge and appreciate the quality attention that women give to other people. Appreciate yourself. Take good care of you.

As you age, you could feel adrift and lost. The roof is leaking, and the garden is being taken over by poison ivy. What if you are quite worried about your last years? How are you going to manage your finances? What will your days and nights bring you? Unfortunately, hard times are here for many older women who have been undervalued and underpaid all their lives. Now old and alone, they must make their slender resources last. You may have serious social and financial problems this Guide cannot begin to resolve. Reaching out to other woman in parallel straits may be one approach to dealing with these economic challenges. Consider starting an organization and speaking up. The wolf is at the door.

You may be involved in your career or be employed even after you reach retirement age. Many of us will need to keep working to balance our checkbooks, help our families, or be able to afford a vacation. Myself, as a mature artist, I am delighted to continue to work. My career took a long time to establish. Finally my business has momentum, and my creations have an audience. Making art gives me great pleasure. I will continue to produce and exhibit until the very last moment.

Some of the women reading this guide may justifiably want to stop working and can easily reformulate their life by starting to relax, travel, play with the dog, and never lift another pot off the stove. You may have the resources and the desire. Retire. This is your special time. Enjoy the moment. Stake out your spot on the beach, read the entire works of Joyce Carol Oates or begin your world tour. *The good life.*

You may have the funds to live in a well-designed senior community that has every comfort, security and recreational feature that you or you and your partner will need for many decades. And this community may also provide a safety net for the possibility of eventual infirmities. Choosing this supported and thoughtfully designed type of residence can be a perfect answer to living as a senior person or a senior couple. Many forms of co-housing answer the needs of older women and are definitely worth consideration.

After contemplating your own existence, you may be quite pleased with how you lead your life. Excellent. For you this is the best of times. I congratulate you and applaud your nature, good luck, financial resources, and the excellent skills that have placed you so comfortably in a benign world. Your only job as you age is to stay aware of the challenges of the physical decline that happens as time flows on. Just remember to keep your body tuned up so you can dance to your own hit song. You may want to continue just as you are to the end of your days. You know exactly who you are and where you fit in your own world.

For some of us there may be a pile of unused life lingering in a dusty corner. Shake off the dust. There is still time to write a great ending. You and I may have to get very creative and innovative about our choices. I feel that most of my existence is in harmony with my true being, but there are parts of it that I definitely would like to refocus. After decades of wishing I had a different body type, some other childhood, and definitely another person's temperament, I now realize that I will be "Claire" for the rest of my life. I think it is time to be good to Claire, and yet demand from her the highest and most evolved behavior. Yes, I need to make some positive changes.

Can we discover a new pathway for ourselves? Together let us find our way.

This is the time for each of us to take charge of our mind, our body and our society. We need to seriously consider a meaningful use of our last decades. Your true nature might take you down an unexpected road.

130

Different from what most people would choose. You may be climbing the highest mountain to meet the divine. You may find meaning as a teacher, become a community organizer, or find your voice as an artist. You may create an entirely original way of living and share it with a grateful population.

Before resolving to make serious alterations in the fabric of our lives, let us take the time to analyze ourselves. Know thyself. What are the special skills you have acquired over your lifetime? What are the wrongs you would like to right? What organizations/clubs/groups feed your soul? Or is it time for you to start an organization that will genuinely meet the needs of a world in peril?

Youth gave us what seemed like an endless future. Most of us now feel the pulse of time and the limits of our existence. **Heads up!** You have the "now" as much as you did at 20. The secret is to claim it. Trust.

Try this. Give quick answers to the five inquires below. Write down your answers on a piece of paper or use the journal at the end of the chapter.

1. What would you like to change about yourself?

2. What would you like to change about the world?

3. What is holding you back?

4. What do you have to contribute?

5. What makes you happy?

I have included a journal format at the end of the chapter (or download the journal from my website) to explore these queries and review your options. Reflect on your answers. Do you see continuity? What surprises you? What could be your first step towards transformation? Self-knowledge is the beginning of self-wisdom. Answering these questions may reveal a pattern to you or inspire change. You can *accept* yourself. You can *celebrate* yourself. You have the ability to *recreate* yourself.

Working the complete journal helped me think about my life. I answered the questions and studied my answers. I learned that the small pleasures: a vase of daffodils, lunch with a friend, or a quiet evening with a great book give dimension and quality to my days. Deep satisfaction comes to me when a project is resolved with brilliance, or I feel a heart connection with another person, or I can make a contribution to my community. As much as I have loved men and feel wistful about romance, I can no longer count on finding a significant other to fill my life with meaning.

Am I espousing a radical rethinking of your life? Maybe. Look at yourself with curiosity and neutrality. Even a subtle reworking of your patterns might take you on an interesting path. There are many ways you could change your mind that would change your life. What might transformation look like? Try to envision a personal evolution that might include something like this:

- Re-educating yourself

- Creating a daily physical or mental practice or both

- Tending to the emotional wounds that have haunted you all your life.

- Seriously working at finding a long-term partner

- Moving to a new town

- Starting your own business

- Recruiting a group of women to live together

- Giving away all your belongings and joining a religious group

- Becoming a political activist

- Moving to Ecuador or some other foreign country

- Running for public office

Seriously, what would it take to enable you to make an alteration in the fabric of your life? What is stopping you?

"Claire, really? Do you actually know any older women who have such made radical shifts in their lifestyle or world view?" Yes, I do know several women I can brag about, real friends with their real names. Be inspired by Pat P., Donna B., Carolyn S. and Josie L.. Here is how they have transformed:

Pat P. was a successful commercial photographer with a devoted clientele. She closed her business and concentrated on her creative life. Today, Pat is a prize-winning artist and a published writer. After Donna B. marketed her software company for a million plus, she joined the Peace Corp. Last year, Donna went to India for six months to become a certified yoga instructor. She became calmer, slimmer and younger. Carolyn S. sold her house in Florida and built a brilliant "small" home in a co-housing community. She moved to a town where she knew absolutely no one. Today, Carolyn is an integral part of her new neighborhood, blessing all with her zest and ebullience. Josie L., a psychotherapist, found the courage to fight for world peace. Brave and irreverent, she continues to battle the establishment even if it means time in jail. Myself, I renewed my former acquaintance with punctuation and grammar to communicate what I had learned about aging. Instead of crafting art with my hands, I spent two years reading and writing; gaining insight and ten pounds in the process.

Take the opportunity to live as your true self. It is time to claim your authority, your insight and your skills. I absolutely mean this. Thoughtful and innovative women could make the difference in the survival of the human race. Wake up. Use your famous brain. Shift the energy. Explore the pain. Find the vitality. Heads up. ***Your time is now.***

WE SIGH AND TAKE A LONG BREATH.

Let us take a moment to reflect on the state of other women all over the earth.

When my mother was born in 1910, women in the USA did not have the vote. I was born in 1946. As a female, I had the birthright to vote. My expectations for myself as a young woman included the hope for a romantic partnership, a college degree, and the freedom to choose and pursue a career. I explored my sexuality before marriage; I easily obtained birth control to prevent an unwanted pregnancy. Later, I had the option

134

for a safe, legal abortion. I understood that if my marriage failed I could divorce my husband and be allowed to raise my children. I learned to drive and owned an automobile. I traveled by myself. I had my own bank account. I started a business.

As a widow, I have independently controlled my career, my property and my money. Since my husband died, I have had sexual relationships with several men. My neighbors, the local villagers, did not stone me.

You and I live in the 21st century. Take advantage of it. All over this beleaguered earth, girls, wives, mothers, and grandmothers still live in the dark ages. **Still enslaved.**

Women are often victimized by war or civil unrest, cruel ideology, and stagnant chauvinistic cultures. I believe that the world will never be sane until all females have rights equal to all males. Prosperity follows equality. Peace follows prosperity.

All women deserve access to education, political office, jobs, and health care. Included in the appendix is a document that I created entitled "Thirteen Rights—A Global Bill of Rights for Women". I wrote this to explore and define what I see as the fundamental civil liberties that should be the birthright of every female person on this earth.

A society that promotes women's rights and parity is a healthy and flourishing society. When we study any culture in which woman are treated equally, we discover that it is a stable and relatively nonviolent community.

Iceland might be the best place in the world to be female. Iceland leads the world in women's liberty. The United States is ranked 23rd. After a huge banking crisis and collapse in 2007, Iceland's economy is recovering with only four percent unemployment. Looking good for both women and men. I do not recommend that you move to Saudi Arabia. In Saudi Arabia, women are going to be allowed to vote for the first time in 2015. Women are allowed to own cars in Sad Arabia, but not to drive them. Their husbands, fathers and sons are going to be thrilled to drive their ladies to the polls. In 2015, the only sovereign state in the world that denies women a vote will be the Vatican.

Can we (*Femina sapiens)* give our thoughtfulness and our love to a world in crisis? Can we redefine cultures without losing the distinct flavors that give wonderful variety to human life? Can we rescue our younger sisters? Can older women save the earth?

When you purchased this book, 20 percent of the sales price went into an endowment fund entitled "Making It A Better World for Woman and Children". This fund will contribute to carefully selected organizations that strive to bring freedom and equality to the oppressed woman of the world. I will die happy if I know I have left this world a safer place for other women.

Let us create a just and fair reality for all the

women of the world.

Should we sit in our rocking chairs, or stand up and get to work?

Continuing the Conversation

Suggested Readings: *I fully acknowledge that after reading the following books and thinking about the information that is presented, you may come to completely different conclusions than I did.*

Aging with Grace—What the Nun Study Teaches Us about Leading Longer, Healthier and More Meaningful Lives written by David Snowdon, Ph.D., published by Bantam Books.

David Snowdon is an epidemiologist (one that studies patterns of diseases) who is interested in Alzheimer's disease. He realized that studying nuns, who live very regulated lives and keep scrupulous records, would be an ideal research group. In addition, he knew that many nuns live long and often remain very active into old age. He contacted a group of nuns (the School Sisters of Notre Dame) and they graciously agreed to assist him in his research. This meant that the ladies would be studied and tested during their lifetimes, and that after their deaths they would donate their brains for continued investigation. David fell in love (platonic) with his research subjects. This is a charming book and a good read. The author distills his 20-year experience with this group of nuns into advice for living long and well. And I learned that if I make it to 95 without dementia, then more than likely, I will not lose my memories or my train of thought. But, honestly, do I want to live until I am 95?

The Longevity Project: Surprising Discoveries for Health and Long Life from the Landmark Eight-Decade Study written by Howard S. Friedman, Ph.D., and Leslie R. Martin, Ph.D., published by Plume.

The original study of over 1,500 California children was begun by

Dr. Lewis Terman in 1921, and was later continued by other research teams to cover the lifetimes (this included folks who lived to be over 90) of the subjects of the study. This long-term endeavor allows us to have a rare view of how our personality affects our longevity.

One conclusion of the most recent group of researchers is: "Exercise, diet, stress, and weight are indeed relevant to health, but in ways that vary from person to person." The *Termanators* (their name for themselves) studied personality traits and how these traits affect our life span. "The finding clearly revealed that the best childhood personality predictor of longevity was conscientiousness—the qualities of a prudent, persistent, well-organized person." The studies also showed that human beings have the ability to, and in some cases do, change detrimental early childhood patterns. In my general reading, I discovered the research in *The Longevity Project* has been transcribed by many authors and used in their text. This is an original. Worth reading and re-reading.

The Happiness Project written by Gretchen Rubin, published by Harper.

I am in love with this book. When I first discovered it I bought copies for my friends. Gretchen seriously addresses the issue of finding more laughter in your life. Smile—you will be happier, live longer and people will like you better. I really appreciate her encouragement to eliminate the clutter in your life. And she is so forward thinking that she actually enjoys having money. I hope she is making a very tidy pile of greenbacks, selling her well thought-out concepts and suggestions.

Outliers: The Story of Success written by Malcolm Gladwell, published by Back Bay Books.

Once in a great while, someone comes along who thinks so finely, writes so eloquently, and is so amazingly original that you just gasp. Gasp. Meet Malcolm Gladwell. He toys with many ideas because he can. He talks about how cultural values affect behavior. And how effort, time well spent,

138

being at the right place at the right time, support, and connection correlate with success. And how success may ultimately be defined by meaningful work. I encourage you to become a fan and read everything he writes.

__Crones Don't Whine, Concentrated Wisdom for Juicy Women__ written by Jean Shinoda Bolen, M.D., published by Conari Press.

This author, very famous in women's empowerment circles, has a beautiful way with words and phrases. However, I admit I grew fatigued by the endlessly repeated use of *crone*. But if we can accept her jargon and spend time with this slim volume, we gain a finely tooled book, dedicated to older women, about our potential and our place in the world. Here is a juicy quote from her book: "Truth is sharp-edged: it is an instrument that can cause pain, wound, disfigure, or maim. Or, it can be a surgeon's scalpel that removes a malignancy or reconstructs a damaged face, and restores health or self-esteem." `

Useful Websites:

__www.amodernwomansguide.com__

You can go to my website to download any journals or forms that I have included in the guide. I will share anything new I learn about aging with frequent updates and thoughts.

Co-Housing: If you are interested in co-housing, here are websites that have information and recommendations:

- *www.ic.org*

- *www.cohousing.org*

- Following the lead of *Golden Girls*, you might find two or three other women with whom you can create a group household: *www.wncwoman.com*

And if you have a strong desire to be ecologically correct in your environment, check out: *www.motherearthliving.com/green*

Are you a caregiver looking for support?

Here is a place to start: *www.caregiveraction.org*

Do you want more help in your journey of self-discovery?

Here is a place to begin: *www.manifestyourpotential.com*

You may be interested in joining one of these organizations for global women's rights:

- *www.vday.org*

- *senecawomen.com*

- *www.feminist.org*

A couple more interesting sites:

If you want to learn about women who are unusually successful or important. you can click on: *www.makers.com*

Are you feeling lonely? Need advice? Here is a soft, friendly, and helpful site: *sixtyandme.com*

Search for meaning and purpose: What truly matters to you?

Answering these 27 questions (no, it is not too many) is simply an aid to self-reflection and not meant to encourage self-recrimination. **Your goal is self-knowledge.** No one but you will ever read what you have written. You are not being graded. Stay neutral and honest. Make your answers are as brief or extensive as you are inspired to make them. Consider responding to all the questions.

1. When are you the most physically comfortable?

2. What are your best attributes?

3. What are you afraid of?

4. What do you need to feel supported?

5. What would you like to learn?

6. What has been so far the happiest time of your life?

7. Do you enjoy sex?

8. Who do you want to make love to?

9. What would you like to change about the world?

10. What makes you laugh?

11. Who have you harmed?

12. Who have you helped?

13. What relationships feed you?

14. What is holding you back?

15. What is pushing you forward?

16. What are your biggest regrets?

17. What is your biggest achievement so far?

18. Who do you love?

19. Who do you hate?

20. If you could rename yourself, what would you call yourself?

21. What gives you joy?

22. What do you miss about being young?

23. What do you like about yourself?

24. What do you *like* about getting older?

25. What do you *dislike* about getting older?

25. And what makes you *happy?*

26. What was the biggest surprise in the last decade?

27. What would you like to change about yourself?

WHAT TO DO WITH YOUR RESPONSES:

I found this journal exercise was a poignant technique to explore my inner workings. I am not the same *me* as I was at 30 or I was at 40 or even at 50. You may want to put this exercise aside and look at your responses another day. Or you may be eager to review what you just wrote. Whenever you decide to read your answers to the questions, spend some time with your thoughts. What surprised you? What did you learn about yourself? You may feel totally comfortable with who you are and how your life has unfolded. Sincere congratulations. Or you may feel that life as you are living it could use some reshaping.

If you feel that a judicious redesigning of your existence would be wonderful, then how would you advise yourself to take action or change your life pattern? *What is the first step you could take?*

CLAIRE'S RECIPE: DIRECTIONS FOR MAKING LASAGNA:

The secret to cooking a great lasagna is this: the better the ingredients, the better the dish. This lasagna will serve 8 to 10 people. This dish feels complete served with a green salad and crusty bread. If you invite your teenage grandchildren with enormous appetites, you can bake a few pounds of Italian sausage as a side dish. Make with love.

What you need to successfully make this dish:

A large (9" x 13") baking or lasagna pan

A large pot for cooking noodles

A Dutch oven or large pan with a cover

A large bowl for the ricotta mixture

Foil

2 onions—finely chopped

3 large gloves of garlic—finely minced

Two large cans of whole tomatoes

One small can of tomato paste

4 medium eggs: In a cup, stir up raw eggs until mixture is a uniform yellow

Fresh parsley—½ cup, finely chopped

Fresh basil—½ cup, finely chopped

Nutmeg—1 ground teaspoon or 10 grinds

Italian seasoning (dried)—2 teaspoons for sauce

Pepper—1 teaspoon or 5 grinds

Red pepper flakes, if you like a spicier sauce—1 teaspoon

Salt—2 teaspoons (1 teaspoon for sauce & 1 for ricotta mixture)

Sugar—1 tablespoon for sauce

1 box lasagna noodles

Ricotta—2 pounds

Mozzarella—2 pounds, sliced into ¼-in. slices

Parmesan—8 ounces

Olive oil—2 ounces (1/4-cup), plus a few tablespoons

1 cup water or red wine

Optional: Spinach—1 box of defrosted frozen chopped spinach, which you can chop finer if desired

- *Preheat the oven to 375 F (190 C).*

1. If you plan to include spinach in the ricotta mixture, then set out the frozen chopped spinach to defrost. Each of these ingredients can be put on small, separate plates. Mince the garlic, chop onions, basil, and parsley. Open the cans of tomatoes and tomato paste. In a large pan, heat ¼ cup of olive oil to a medium temperature. Cook the onion and garlic over medium heat until well-browned, golden in color, but not burnt. Stir in crushed tomatoes, tomato paste, and water or red wine. Season with sugar, Italian seasoning, 1 teaspoon of salt, pepper, and 2 to 3 tablespoons parsley. If you like your sauce spicier, add a teaspoon of crushed red pepper. Simmer your sauce in the now covered pan for about an hour. Stir the sauce occasionally and, if needed, thin with wine or water. The sauce

Should be thin enough to easily fill a large spoon—just slightly thicker than soup.

2. Bring a large pot of lightly salted water to a boil. Cook lasagna noodles in boiling water for 12 to 15 minutes. The noodle should be cooked but still quite firm. Drain noodles, and rinse with cold water. Set aside.

3. In a mixing bowl, combine ricotta cheese with eggs, remaining parsley, 2 tablespoons of fresh basil, ground nutmeg and teaspoon salt. Mix thoroughly with a large spoon or your hands. If you like the color green, you can add chopped spinach or more chopped parsley for color and flavor. Mix and set aside.

4. To assemble, oil the bottom of a 9 x 13" pan, and spread 1-1/2 cups of red sauce in the bottom of the dish. Arrange 4 or 5 noodles lengthwise over sauce. Spread with half the ricotta cheese mixture. Top with a third of mozzarella cheese slices. Spoon 1-1/2 cups tomato sauce over mozzarella, and sprinkle with ¼-cup Parmesan cheese. Put down another 3 or 4 noodles. Add another layer of tomato sauce, ricotta, mozzarella and Parmesan as above. Then top with remaining noodles, sauce, and cheese. Sprinkle with the rest of the chopped fresh basil and parsley. Cover with foil. (To prevent sticking, either spray foil with cooking spray, or make sure the foil does not touch the cheese.)

5. Bake in preheated oven (375 F) for 30 minutes. You can spend this time cleaning up the big mess you have made of your kitchen. Remove foil and bake an additional 30 minutes. Time for a short rest. I am referring to you. The sauce and the cheese should now be bubbling and hot. Take the lasagna out of the oven. Cover the lasagna again with foil. Cover the entire dish with a clean towel. Let it rest. This time I am referring to the lasagna. Let the lasagna settle for 30 minutes before serving.

THIRTEEN RIGHTS—A GLOBAL BILL OF WOMEN'S RIGHTS

In my own search for meaning, this is a document I composed, feeling I needed to do something, say something, or write something. This is my ideal of what real equality would look like in a world that I wished existed but may never. The long version of this bill of rights is included in the Appendix.

The website is *13rights.com.*

1. The right to vote in all elections.

2. Equal representation in the government.

3. The right to assemble and access to communication.

4. The right to education.

5. Freedom of movement.

6. Freedom of marriage or non-marriage.

7. The right to carry weapons for protection.

8. The right to own property.

9. Equal rights, pay, and access to work.

10. The right to choice of physical appearance.

11. The right to birth control.

12. The right to safely terminate a pregnancy.

13. The sanctity of our female genitals.

Thoughts.......

Thoughts……

Thoughts…...

Thoughts…...

Thoughts…...

Thoughts……

Chapter Five: Love Your Dentist and Other Thoughts

I have spent decades in this body, and I am still not sure who is in charge. Or exactly how to take care of me.

My automobile comes with a manual. I learned to drive late in life, but I soon figured out that I should change the oil every five thousand miles, that the tires should be rotated and balanced, and that it was unwise to ignore strange and unfamiliar noises emerging from the car engine.

My physical body seems trickier and more mysterious. Years ago while depilating my legs (why do women try to be as hairless as a child?) preparing for a beach vacation, I noticed an odd-looking mole. I took myself to the dermatologist. We were both surprised that it was a *melanoma*. A small cancer had started to quietly grow on my leg without causing me any discomfort. I caught the *melanoma* early in its cycle and with two minor surgeries was able to go on with my life. It easily could have been a different story.

Puberty, pregnancy, childbirth, and menopause have all caused startling physical alterations. Often I have been unprepared and taken aback by my body's ongoing metamorphoses. Without instructions from me, it has changed shape, grown pubic hair, bled, swelled, lactated, ceased to bleed, changed shape again, and now it is aching and stiffening. What the hell! How can I take charge of this precious container?

Modern older women have unprecedented opportunities to employ the tools of science, medicine, alternative care and dentistry to continue a healthy existence in our vintage years. In this chapter, let us do our best to assess what is available to us to take care of our bodies inside and out, from the seemingly *superficial* to the *profoundly complex*. We will focus on the care of our bodies from head to toe.

SMILE. HOW ARE YOUR TEETH?

Nothing will age you more than your teeth or lack of them.

Yes, dental care is not cheap. But it is a great investment in your health and your looks. At the risk of seeming quite senior and repeating myself, I am going to quote Chapter 1:

"Our teeth are wearing down and may appear darker or discolored. Teeth cannot repair themselves, so a tooth once chipped, broken or missing needs the attention of the dentist. Nothing ages our facial appearance more than losing our teeth or having bone loss in our jaw. Gum disease is much more of a threat to general health then was once commonly believed. The condition of your gums affects your entire body, including your heart."

Prioritize regular visits to the dentist. Keep your gums healthy. Brush your teeth after every meal. Floss daily. Purchase an electric toothbrush or a water pic. Use these modestly priced devices. Be a tough parent to yourself—the teeth you save may be your own. Have your teeth professionally cleaned regularly. Yes, love your dental hygienist.

A great smile with well-maintained teeth will improve your appearance. Consider whitening your teeth, straightening your teeth, getting crowns, implants, proper bridges, or—if needed—dentures. Save your coins. Buy dental insurance. Sell your mother-in-law's gold jewelry. Locate a dental school and offer yourself as a friendly subject. Give us your best smile and show off your well-kept mouth.

As a mature woman, shouldn't I be comfortable looking my age? Hmmm. I have noticed that in the last few years the one compliment that will make me suck in my stomach, fluff my hair, and stand up straighter is: "You cannot possibly be_____; you look ten years younger." Why do many of us want to look like menopause never happened? Simple answer: because we live in a culture that worships youth.

Modern women can look "not our age," because we have options that were not available to our ancestors. I am referring to those ladies who wandered the savannahs of times gone by or even our grandmas in old family photos with bosoms held up by the waistbands of their aprons, crinkly cheeks, and faces framed by whispers of white hair.

You can dye your hair any color you want. You can buy quality color kits at the grocery store or go to the beauty salon. How many women over fifty alter their hair color? Plenty. Changing your hair color is the least invasive method you can use to erase the signs of aging. However, dear reader, you may enjoy your grey or white hair and look quite fetching. Suddenly you are in style. My hair is still naturally dark. At least for now, I like the strands of silver among the brown.

Look at your face in a mirror. You may not like what you see.

What's happening? Most of the damage to our skin is from exposure to the sun. Now, take a look at your naked rear end in a mirror. *What?* Well this part of your body has not had a great deal of sun exposure unless you have a time-share at a nudist colony. *Surprise.* The skin on your nether region is in much better shape than your complexion that has been out and about. Sunscreen is available at the drug store, the grocery store and the convenience store. And don't forget to wear a hat.

Make an appointment with a dermatologist. The areas that have seen too much sun may look and feel worn. And you need to be checked for pre-cancerous or cancerous changes to your skin. While you are at the dermatologist you can have a conversation about improving the look of your complexion. Your dermatologist can help you refresh your skin with prescription products that contain Retina A. However, you will have to be a very compliant patient who strictly follows instructions.

Trying to look livelier and more youthful? You may want to start putting on a face. Makeup. *Why not?* It works for film stars and models. Enter the new world of glamour. Consult the lovely, 20-year-old salesperson in a cosmetic specialty shop. She will be glad to advise you. Any resemblance to elderly actresses with badly applied lipstick and peculiar eyebrows is to be carefully avoided. I suggest purchasing a magnifying mirror to apply your "paint" skillfully.

And then there are the myriad creams and lotions to keep your skin moist. Easy to buy and difficult to select. Finding a great over-the-counter product for your complexion will take research and experimentation. Cost is not always a sure guide. A friend of mine, Susan, who died in her nineties, had wonderful skin even after living for years in a dry climate. One day she whispered to me, "Vaseline. "

Pinky (my mother) wore heavy makeup every day of her life. She never went to bed without removing the "paint" and creaming her face with Revlon's *Eterna 27*. Pinky aka Grandma B. aka Beatrice died at 84 without a line in her smooth face. She did not look young. She did not look old. She just looked seamless.

Pinky was a histrionic (think drama) and a wounded narcissist... I wonder how my psychotherapist daughter would diagnosis me? Anyway, I thought of my mother's entrenched self-involvement as a wall between us. I felt it prevented her from being emotionally available. When Pinky was in her 75th year, I visited her apartment in New York City. Observing my mother, I realized that she was paying marvelous attention to the details. Her flaws (yes, my perception) were turning into virtues. Her dyed hair was coiffed. Her clothes were clean and stylish. She wore her dentures. Her cosmetics were applied with care. She had created a beautiful environment. Mom was current on the state of the world. I thought, "My mother is going to stay crisp to the end." She did.

I have witnessed the other end of the spectrum. I call it "embracing the crone." Sans teeth, uncombed hair, dirty nails, stained clothes, and a faint odor of rust.

I do not feel that I need to look *ancient* to be an empowered older woman. I hope to continue to look attractive even if takes more effort and money than when I was 40 or even 50 years old. You may choose a very "let it happen" attitude towards your appearance. Yes, I know some women go to "Oh my gawd, what was she thinking?" extremes to look not their age.

Why? Because we live in a society in which women are valued based on youthfulness, thinness, and beauty. The external consequences of the natural aging process may upset us and make us feel at a disadvantage socially, romantically, or in the workplace. There can be a balanced position. You may want to embrace some of the cosmetic choices that are on the menu of holding back Mother Time. *Or not.*

Here is list of procedures (not cheap) that might make you look less senior, but of course do not alter aging on the cellular level. However, if you are more confident about your appearance, won't you stay alive longer or at least want to? And, yes, the glow of health, proper exercise, good posture, the right diet, and the empowerment of the well-chosen life pathway will affect how you appear to other people and how people respond to you.

COSMETIC RELIEF:

1. The classic: A *facelift* is a procedure done under general anesthetic with the risks and recovery period of any serious surgery. Gravity's tugging causes a sliding of your face towards your feet. A facelift can reverse the drop and give a more youthful appearance.

A facelift addresses the sagging of the underlying muscles in your face as well as tightening the loose and wrinkled surface skin. Performed by a plastic surgeon who specializes in the face, the scars should be imperceptible, and the results last ten years and beyond.

2. Less invasive: An *eyelift* can brighten your face and open your eyes. Eyelift procedures tackle the aging of the upper lid of the eye and/or the lower lid of the eye or both. The upper eyelid may have lost enough elasticity so that your skin droops over your eyeball and affects your vision. If you have this condition, then reconstructing the lid is considered a medical procedure and is covered by insurance.

The surgery that deals with the lower lid can also address the puffy fat under the eye that occurs in some mature faces. If overdone, this can result in an excessively hollow area under the eye. Having both the upper and lower eyelid addressed may improve your appearance. If done by an expert, the tiny stitches will be hidden in the folds of the lid. As the area around your eye is very thin-skinned, bruising and discoloration may extend your recovery time.

3. Surprisingly common: *Liposuction* permanently removes fat cells. Lipo can be done to address areas that exercise and diet have not improved. Fat deposits on the belly and thighs are common storage points on a female body—useful as a hedge against lean times but not so welcome to modern women. Liposuction is not recommended as a way to lose weight. A tube is inserted under the skin, and fat cells are sucked away. The aftermath is quite messy with blood and fluid seeping from the ports where the tubes were inserted. The patient usually does not experience significant pain. The results vary according to the skill of the doctor. This may be a procedure better done before you reach 50 as older skin may sag or pit. There is a three-to-four week recovery period.

4. Very common: *Botox* (botulin toxin, a protein that relaxes muscle) temporarily paralyzes the muscles that are causing frown lines or wrinkles. Basically it rests the area and fine wrinkles will soften. Best used for frown lines and crow's feet. This is a safe procedure done in the doctor's office. Your body eventually reabsorbs Botox, so to maintain your smooth appearance, you will need injections every three to four months. Over a year, the cost will accumulate. Try thinking happy thoughts.

5. This might be the answer: *Peels* come in various strengths of chemicals or are performed with lasers that remove layers of skin. The healing grows younger-looking epidermis and may improve collagen. Mild forms of exfoliation can be done as an outpatient with only a few days of noticeably red and irritated skin. Severe lines can be dealt with by a more extensive removal of layers of skin. This deep peel must be done under anesthesia with weeks of downtime and months of healing.

6. Hollywood or bust: *Breast implants* are silicone or saline packs that are inserted under the muscle or under the skin to increase the size of the breasts. If you have always wanted beautiful size D's, this could be a "happy change" for your self-image. I suggest you do some research. Who in your area creates the best bosom? Results vary. Ask to see before and after photos. If your friend will admit to having work, ask to see her

166

after photos. If your friend will admit to having work, ask to see her breasts. May the best boobs win.

7. Small and perky: *Reducing the breast size* may be a relief to women who suffer from backache and poor posture due to the size of their breast. However, this is major surgery. The nipples will be removed or partially severed from the breast. They will be repositioned. The reduction will also include reshaping of the muscle layer and removal of loose skin. The surgeon may decide to augment the upper breast to create a more balanced appearance. There are the risks of any major surgery and weeks of downtime. For some, the risks, pain, and scars are definitely worth it. If you can establish that there are detrimental health and posture problems caused by your heavy bosom, then you might get your insurance company to pay for the procedure.

8. Always ready to go out: *Permanent make up* is a form of tattooing. You can darken your eyebrows, or underline your eyes or even color your lips. Dark eyebrows may make your face look more alive and counter the washed-out look that often comes with aging. This is mildly painful with a few days recovery time. If you want to have this done, choose a person who makes permanent makeup their full-time profession. Avoid your local beautician who learned this technique in a weekend workshop. The results should last for years.

9. Injectables: *Fillers* are a kind of putty to fill in deep lines on your face especially around your mouth or chin. This procedure plumps up areas that have given your face a severe or unhappy look. Various products are available through your licensed dermatologist. These substances are safe with a small chance of reaction.

Your own fat can be injected in these lines. There is more expense involved in this approach, as your fat has to be drawn from your hip or belly and then treated before it is injected into your face. If you harvest your own fat you will not only have a zero risk of reaction, but the result will be longer lasting.

10. Smoothing it out: *Microdermabrasion & micro needling, radio waves, and lasers* are all ways to basically sand your face. This means taking a few layers of skin off to improve texture and soften or eliminate lines. Mild versions of this treatment can be done without any down time. To get more face-changing results, you will need to make four to six visits, all within a few months time. More dents in your budget, but a younger-looking face.

11. Keeping up with the latest: *New cosmetic processes* are always being developed. Lots of money to be made. As a curious consumer you may want to be aware of what is the latest "dish" on the "keep me looking good" menu. Fashion and women's magazine do a great job of keeping us informed of the advances in this field.

All of the "Make me look thirty again!" procedures I have

described, do have some hazards, and they are not always cosmetically successful. It is your choice, your funds, your decision, and your risk. And may I add, it is your body.

Can we agree not to judge each other for the efforts we go to retain a semblance of our youth and our beauty?

Let us leave these intriguing or *awful* cosmetic solutions (depending on how you view them) and begin to explore our less elective and perhaps inevitable interactions with the healthcare community.

Are you pleased with the medical care you presently are receiving? Terrific? Mediocre? Okay? Like me, you may feel the care is adequate, but the attitude could use some work. Most of us do not get to express our needs, feelings, and concerns to our medical and dental providers.

Modern doctors are worried about being sued. Dentists are worried about getting AIDS from our blood. All of them are carefully timing our sessions. And all of them (including the alternative practitioners) need to make money. Many of them are desperate to pay off school loans; their insurance rates are crazy, they may have to pay alimony, and their overhead is high.

Dissatisfied with the service and/or the results we get from visiting the local mainstream medicine crew, many of us visit chiropractors, acupuncturists, naturopaths, and homeopaths. We often are paying them out of our own funds since they do not take insurance. We want solutions to health problems the conventional medical establishment is not addressing. Another reason we choose their services is we are hoping for personal attention. Quality attention.

I spent a year contributing to the finances of several well-loved local chiropractors, acupuncturists, and a witch doctor (joke). I went because I was in a considerable amount of pain and could hardly use my left shoulder. I enjoyed their hands-on treatments. My pain was relieved... for a few hours. They all were delighted to make me another appointment, "Ok, Claire, I can see you next Wednesday at two." What I did not hear from any of them was: "You are not getting better. I do not know what is wrong with you. You need to see a medical doctor."

Reluctantly, I went to the orthopedic clinic. Of course, I had to fill out forms that no one will ever consult, wait, sit in an exquisitely uncomfortable chair, wait, stare at other dejected patients, wait, and read *Stream and Fish Magazine* from start to finish. Finally, a nurse put me in a small cold room. Now, quite alone, I sat there. Chilled. I sat there, until a young athletic-looking doctor finally came in the room. He spoke briefly to me and examined my disabled left shoulder.

The doctor insisted on an X-ray, which he found inconclusive. Next, I had to make an appointed for a MRI (Magnetic Resonance Imaging). Eventually, I received the verdict. Bone loss and arthritis in my shoulder. Cause unknown.

I was sent to physical therapy. I went ten times—the amount my insurance covered. I learned how to compensate for my fragile shoulder and to find new muscles to do the work. Marcia, my therapist, was tough and honest. She was also demanding. I got much better. For the first time in two years, I could fasten my own seatbelt without using my right hand and my teeth.

Yes, I have just described my personal experience. You may be getting wonderful results from your alternative practitioners. Certainly, you may find that pain and stress management are much better served outside the conventional doctor's office.

On the subject of different approaches to improving our wellbeing, meditation, at one time, was considered very eccentric. No longer. Meditation has been shown to have many health benefits and has gained acceptance as a tool for pain relief and stress reduction. Jon Kabat-Zinn, a scientist with all the right credentials, including a Ph.D. from MIT (Massachusetts Institute of Technology), established with rigorous studies that "mindfulness" could have a positive effect on our health. His 1993 book, *Wherever You Go, There You Are*—the A-to-Z book on meditation—was a bestseller. Today his methods are valued and used by health care professionals all over the globe. Creating your own "mindful" practice will take patience and self-discipline, but it could alter your perceptions and improve your health.

Find the caregivers (of any stripe) who suit your needs, just remember who is in charge. *You.* The question that needs an honest answer is: ***"Is this treatment really making a difference in my health and wellbeing?"*** And that goes for vitamins, supplements and herbs as well. Are you feeding your body, the plumbing, or the bank account of the manufacturer? Many of the studies done on the value of vitamins and herbs are inconclusive. Vitamin D is an exception. Very few of us in our indoor culture produce enough Vitamin D. Our early ancestors lived nearly naked in the sunshine zones and that is why our bodies are still greedy for Vitamin D.

Get your Vitamin D level tested and, if necessary, take D-3 to bring it to an optimal level (50-70 ng/ml). There is little danger of overdosing yourself. Vitamin D is present in every tissue and cell of your body. There is strong evidence that it helps the body absorb calcium (one of bone's main building blocks) from food and lowers our risk of chronic disease.

Of course, your body and your health are affected by your food and vitamin intake. Often the complexity of organic compounds that occur in nature are not fully duplicated by brown jars of supplements that you purchase in the vitamin section of the grocery store.

What to do? You can try various supplements, herbs and vitamins. Find your inner-scientist. Use the journal (after this chapter or at www.amodernwomensguide.com) and track your 30-day response. At the end of 30 days ask yourself, "*Do I feel better, worse, or no different?*"

You could just take a high quality multi-vitamin. Eat a great deal of fruits and vegetables. And exercise.

What if you suffer from high blood pressure, diabetes, osteoporosis, high cholesterol, or heart disease? Take the pills you have been prescribed, but also make a concerted effort to change. Study Chapter 2 which covers how you can improve your relationship to food and Chapter 3 on how exercise contributes to your health. Make a plan for a stronger, healthier you. Find the will power. Do the work. If you implement a lifestyle transformation, you will reduce or eliminate your need for drugs. You can be an active vital older woman.

How about vaccinations? The subject gives me a headache. I am very grateful that my mother decided I should have the polio vaccine as soon as it became available. Here's something without controversy: Get a tetanus shot! Prevents lockjaw (something no woman wants).

Flu shots? I confess that I have never had a flu shot. I get ill every other winter. I read all the books I have not had time for and swig chicken soup. Do you want/need to get flu shots or other immunizations? Consult a professional that you respect and trust. Can't find one? *Hmmm....* And yes, here you are again making another decision about managing your own physical condition.

When it comes to your general health, your body may exhibit the signs that it is undergoing an aging process. Or not—lucky you. I believe a cautious awareness of our vulnerability is a sensible approach to seeking help from the worlds of medical and alternative care. I do not believe you must go to the doctor even just for the yearly "checkup." However, if your body is complaining, or is changing in odds ways, or even whispering that things are not feeling right, you need to **pay attention** and make an effort to understand the cause or causes.

You may already have had a major health issue or a lifesaving operation. You might already be dealing with a chronic condition. At this moment, you may be enjoying excellent health. However, it is very likely that you will eventually need some care from a doctor. And doctors are very special. Most contemporary doctors are specialists. You may have to visit a long list of different professionals to understand how your whole body is faring.

PARTNERS IN SICKNESS AND HEALTH:

1. The starting point: Our internist, primary physician, nurse practitioner, or physician's assistant (PA) is the person you go to if you have the flu. Or for your shingles vaccination. Think of this person as your coordinator or your main squeeze. Please find a professional who you can talk to and respects your wishes. If it is needed, you will receive a recommendation to see a specialist. And you may need a referral to get beyond the specialist's well-guarded gate.

2. You know this one. The *gynecologist* is the one doctor most women visit throughout their lifetime. After all, our vaginas and our wombs are very precious parts specific to the female body—your body. *I believe women deserve the freedom to decide the uses of these parts.* As a senior woman, your womb is no longer a functioning organ. Mine has shriveled-up and left town. And if you are over 65, and your last three pap smears are negative, you can forget about it—no more pap smears needed. Unless you are bleeding or having an unusual discharge, then run to the doctor's office.

Are you a candidate for HRT? **H**ormone **R**eplacement **T**herapy—a great solution or a threat to your health? HRT will certainly lessen meno-pausal systems. You may want to take HRT right after menopause for five years. Certain cancers feed on estrogen, but estrogen with progesterone may keep the post-menopausal woman at lower risk for heart disease, for memory loss, and for osteoporosis. Some studies that say you will be protected from heart disease by taking hormones, and there are other studies that say hormones increase your risk for strokes and cancer. Some relief of symptoms is reported from wild yam and maca. If these gentle foods work for you, all to the good. However, the research is not convincing. Hmmm.... Consult your doctor or alternative practitioner who may be as confused as you are? Coin toss?

What about the problems specific to the elderly vagina? Are you experiencing more pain than pleasure during sexual intercourse?
Talk to your gynecologist. If you are experiencing thinning of the wall of your vagina, you may be prescribed a topical estrogen cream. This may relieve your discomfort.

Low-dose estrogen cream has very little health-risk unless you have had breast cancer. Alternatively you can use over-the-counter lubricants or moisturizers.

Many senior citizens still enjoy sexual relations. And some don't. *But many do.* Certain gentlemen are motivated to take Viagra or similar drugs. An amazing erection that lasts for four hours (as exciting as it is for the average man) may not be something that interests the average woman. If you get the right grease and he takes the right pill, then the two of you will have a lovely time together. However if your aging male partner is experiencing some form of mild erectile dysfunction, it might be time to learn some new lovemaking skills. This could be very stimulating for both of you.

You may be a newly single woman hoping to embark on sexual adventures. Warning: It is a much more dangerous world out there than when you were single back in the '60s. Practice *sage sex*—be wise. Use condoms. You are never too old to get Herpes or AIDS. Practice and ask for honesty.

Enjoy the intimacy. Learn new ways. Find and give pleasure. You are too old for guilt. Sex is still terrific.

3. You are squinting and trying to tweeze, when you realize you cannot see, the hair growing on your chin. You decide to visit your **ophthalmologist** to adjust your prescription for your eyeglasses. Eventually you may develop a thick and cloudy eye lens, called a cataract, and need surgery to remove this lens and prevent blindness. The good news is that the intraocular lens that is put in when the cataract is removed can also correct another condition such as astigmatism. How wonderful that after your successful surgery, you may see better than you ever have in your life!

4. After many years of doing a splendid job, some of your joints may be wearing out. The **orthopedist** has a busy schedule; however, he or she will find time to visit with you. After years, of tennis, skiing, running and living life, your knees and shoulders may have scar tissue, tears, and rips. You can have laparoscopic surgery. This is generally done on an out-patient basis. The surgeon uses tiny incisions so your body will not react as if it is undergoing a major trauma. Chances are excellent that you will have less pain and a better functioning body.

Do you want to live your last years as a Bionic Woman? Your worn -out parts can be replaced. Hips, knees, shoulders can be made new again—well, almost. The replacement joints are made of metal (usually titanium), ceramic or polyethylene (a type of hard plastic). These materials can be

176

affixed to the bone with acrylic cement, or they can be press-fitted, which allows bone to grow into the implant. And many women get terrific results from these replacements. They are able to do activities that they thought they would have to give up forever. You can plan these surgeries rather than having your hip replaced as an emergency event. Hire a surgeon who does the procedure over and over—every day. Avoid the old family surgeon who loves you, but finished medical school a long time ago.

> Is there a dark side? Yes!
>
> It is major surgery with the risk and recovery of any surgery.
>
> The results may not be as great as you expected.
>
> You will have a foreign object in your body that may increase your
>
> risk of inflammation or infection.

Even with these hazards, many of us will choose an orthopedic procedure if there is a chance it will improve our mobility.

5. Heart disease is the number one killer of woman. You could find yourself seeing a *cardiologist.* The famous comedian, Rosie O'Don- nell, had a massive heart attack and was amazed to find out that her very odd symptoms meant that she should have gone to the emergency room, *immediately,* instead of trying to keep to her schedule. Having barely sur- vived, Rosie is on a mission to bring awareness to other women. She came up with an acronym H.E.P.P.P. (**H**ot, **E**xhausted, **P**ain, **P**ale, **P**uke) to teach the symptoms of a woman having a heart attack. Try sounding out HEPPP—you will probably sputter and giggle, but you will remember it. If you are experiencing fatigue, shortness of breath, fast heartbeat, irregular or noticeable heartbeat, or dizziness, then *please* take yourself to a doctor

or the emergency room. Ignorance is risk.

6. As you age, you are more vulnerable to being struck down by a cerebrovascular accident—otherwise known as a stroke. Monitor your blood pressure. *Be aware of signals from your over-taxed body.* If you have a headache that just won't go away, you cannot sleep, you are experiencing unexplained agitation, or your legs feel numb and tingly and/or you're dizzy you have the right to be concerned. Now is the time to get a referral to visit a **neurologist** before, not after, you have had a stroke.

7. The days of eating cold pizza for breakfast after a night of partying may only be an *"I can't believe it was me"* memory. Your digestive system is changing and becoming more sensitive. You may want to consider a colonoscopy for cancer screening. If polyps (growths in the colon) are found, they can be removed. Yes, the preparation for this test is disgusting; however, colon cancer is one of cancers mostly likely to affect women, and it is curable. If your colon is bright and clean—you needn't return for five years. The expert doctors, the ***gastroenterologist***, and the ***internist***, may be part of this team.

8. If cancer is found, tough times are here. You have an appointment with an ***oncologist***—the specialist who will try to help you conquer your cancer.

9. You may be bored with your patterns of anger, depression, neurotic behavior—the same emotional stuff over and over again. It might

be worth the time and money to find and visit a psychotherapist or a psychiatrist. It is never to late to shine light on the deepest sad places.

10. Head-to-toe health awareness: *What now?* Something weird has happened to your toenails. You may have hardly ever thought about your feet. Now they hurt. Painting your toenails bright colors does not make your feet forgive improperly fitting shoes, fashionable high heels, lack of exercise, or those extra pounds. All these years they have obligingly carried you about. Now they are very tired. As you age you are increasingly vulnerable to bunions and to fungus in your nails (athlete's foot)—nasty business. Tingling and discomfort in your footsies may be signaling the beginning of arthritis and diabetes. Next, you find out that the crazy morning cramping in your feet is *plantar fasciitis*—an inflammation of the ligament that runs along the arch. Visit the ***podiatrist*** to give you advice, topical ointments and, if necessary, surgery. Be very kind to your feet. Let us take proper care of them, so we can walk to the end of our days.

11. And yes, as we discussed at the beginning of this chapter, to take loving care of self, you may find yourself spending quality time with the **dentist**, the **dermatologist** and the **plastic surgeon.**

ALTERNATIVE CARE OPTIONS:

Are the cows healthier and the grass more nourishing on the other side of the road? *Are you curious about the world of alternative care?*
If you have been in a car accident, your insurance will pay for you to visit a ***chiropractor.*** This professional is trained to deal with back pain, neck

pain, and headaches. Chiropractors will inform you that correct alignment in your spine will improve your general health. And it might.

The ancient practice of **acupuncture** may help you with your energy level, stress, and pain. Your acupuncturist uses very thin (sterile) needles and will insert them in very specific points on the body. This treatment is an art/science practiced in China for thousands of years that is steadily gaining popularity in the western world.

Homeopaths encourage the body to heal itself. The homeopath uses remedies (medicines) that are a minuscule amount of the disease or an irritant in order to trigger a precise reaction and engage the body's own curative power. This is a gentle approach to health.

If you want a bridge between all the different realities, you can employ a **naturopathic** *doctor.* Naturopaths have a similar, science-based education to other primary care providers. However, they integrate standard medical diagnostics with a broad range of natural therapies. They can prescribe pharmaceuticals but cannot perform surgeries.

Whew. I am sure that I left somebody out. My apologies.

As we become older, we need dedication. I find that as I age, I need to choose my doctor or acupuncturist with as much thought as my hair stylist, manicurist, or masseuse. We are paying skilled, trained individual fees for their services. This is an exchange of money for value.

Podiatrists, naturopaths, accountants (just seeing if you are still awake), and dentists are our employees. They are certainly not gods. If we are dissatisfied with their services, we have the right to complain and find other folks to do their job. Fire them. It is not a time to be timid, shy, or modest. You deserve the best care.

What if something goes terribly wrong with your health? After living in your body for all these decades, you may realize you are not well. Or a routine examination reveals an end-time illness like cancer, blood clots, an aneurysm (a weakened blood vessel) ready to burst, kidney failure, or some other awful death sentence. How do we manage catastrophic illness? If you are told that you are very sick, the very first thing you might want to do is get a second opinion. If several doctors tell you that you are in trouble, then you will need to resolve how you will handle this crisis.

You can decide to fight or not to fight. You can ask for palliative care. Truly, you do have choices. *You may have a powerful will to live.* Acknowledge it. If you have already thought about how you feel about quality of life issues and your own death, then you will be better able to deal with a major health crisis. *Do not allow anyone to pressure you to do anything you do not want to do.*

If you are going to battle any disease, including cancer, put on your *Wonder Woman* cape and get in touch with your inner Amazon. Tell your caregivers: "Treat me as aggressively as if I were a thirty-year old single mother with two sets of twins under five. Do everything possible to help me stay alive."

Consider this possibility. What would you do if several experts and your family friend, the surgeon, informed you that with *your illness* your chances of living one year were less than your chances of being elected first woman president of the United States? True, you are not a statistic. You are a beautiful special individual who loves and enjoys her life. What do you need to do to fulfill your own sense of purpose? How much time do you need?

Ask yourself, "Do I want to spend the last months of my life being tortured by surgeries, or radiation, or endless examinations, or harsh drugs and/or experimental remedies?"

Ask yourself, "Is the time I might gain from aggressive treatment more or less important to me than facing my own death with courage and a peaceful heart?" Or you may have a different attitude and sincerely declare, "I believe in the power of science and my own will. If I persist, I may be cured." *You will know what is the right path for yourself.*

You are the captain of this team—*you* choose the game plan.
We really need to think about and strategize for the possible disasters that may happen to our bodies and minds. We need to make many sure decisions about terrible times when we are healthy and clear-headed. Let us thoroughly consider this complex subject in the next chapter.

Continuing the Conversation

<u>Suggested Readings:</u> *If you are considering plastic surgery or other cosmetic adventures, the following books will increase your knowledge and aid you in your decision-making process.*

<u>Navigate Your Beauty—Smart and Safe Plastic Surgery Solutions</u> written by Rod J. Rohric, M.D. and Mary Crosland, published by Richmar.

This is a very glossy book that promotes plastic surgery and the other cosmetics procedures covered in this guide. Indeed, it feels like a fancy sales aid. However, the before and after photographs do give you a good idea what plastic surgery might do for your aging face and body.

<u>Face the Facts: The Truth About Facial Plastic Surgery Procedures That Do and Don't Work</u> written by Andrew A. Jacono, MD, FACS, published by Medical Arts Publishing.

This is a slender volume with fewer images and more information than *Navigate Your Beauty.* You can learn a great deal from this tiny guide. The good doctor and famous plastic surgeon, Andrew Jacono, heads a charity to help patients who suffer from facial injury and deformities. Apparently, the skills used to improve our appearance were originally learned on the battlefields to deal with war-ruined faces.

He knows that many of us want to look younger and more attractive, and he encourages women to thoughtfully use the tools of plastic surgery. Dr. Jacono is quite honest about the conditions that cannot be fixed, and informative about the things that can go wrong with your surgery. He makes a sincere attempt to rate creams and lotions. **Yes, he does recommend sunscreen.**

Moving onto other information on diverse, health-related topics:

The Ultimate Guide to Fellatio: How to Go Down on a Man and Give Him Mind-Blowing Pleasure written by Violet Blue, published by Cleis Press.

The title might put you off and, truthfully, the content might shock you. However, this is a serious book with a thorough discussion about the risks of various sexual activities. There is a good chat about the how the penis works, and, never having had one, I am grateful for the information. The book provides specific instructions on how to give pleasure to a male partner. Kinky. Disgusting. *Or–just what your relationship needed?*

The Health Delusion: How to Achieve Exceptional Health in the 21st Century written by Glen Matten, MSc, and Adian Goggins, MSc, published by Hay House.

This book is a sincere attempt to cut through all the hype about diet and supplements. There are two, yes two, chapters on the benefits of Vitamin D. *I told you so.* The authors recommend that we all become a great deal more active, eat more vegetables, eat small amounts of meat and take Vitamin D. OK, let's do it!

Prime Time written by Jane Fonda, published by Random House Trade Papers.

Jane Fonda has written a book for the aging person, *Prime Time*. In this book, we are treated to many stories about Jane Fonda and a whole lot of swell photographs of Jane. I like Jane Fonda, and she is gorgeous at every age, but she is just not representative of the average women. *However,*

184

her celebrity power gives this book an audience it might not otherwise have.

Giving the book its due, Jane does grapple with love, relationship, and sex in the latter years. The book devotes almost 100 pages to the subject, including a section I would call *all you ever wanted to know about erectile dysfunction.* Worth buying for Part Three: "Friendship, Love and Sex."

The Mayo Clinic Book of Alternative Medicine: Straight Answers From the World's Leading Medical Experts, published by Time, Inc.

I recommend you purchase this book as a guide to all things alternative. The guide is easy to read and easy to use. I thought it was a respectful attempt to grapple with the uses of vitamins, supplements, alternative care, and therapeutic approaches. Yoga, Pilates, and Tai Chi all get a green light. Various vitamins and herbs are rated. All the usual encouragements to exercise. I found this book reassuring and trustworthy.

Useful Websites:

www.amodernwomansguide.com

You can always visit my website to download extra journal forms and to learn anything new I have learned about the ever-evolving worlds of medicine and self care.

On Croning:

You may decide to embrace your *crone* self in the most positive way. There is an international women's organization that celebrates older women and has yearly meetings that deal with our issues. Here is how they define crone: "**The word *Crone*,** in its most simplistic sense, designates an old woman, a woman past her childbearing years, a post-menopausal woman. Today, the most common definition of a ***Crone*** is a wise old woman.

Thus, a Crone is a woman who has moved past mid-life and who acknowledges her survivorship, embraces her age, learns from the examined experience of her life, and, most likely, appreciates the wrinkles on her face." You may want to go to one of their gatherings or receive their publications.
www.cronescounsel.org

Cosmetics and Surgery:

You have decided that you are going to give makeup a try, and you want to use the best products for your skin type. Check out this website: *www.sephora.com*

After viewing your most recent photograph, you have decided to consider plastic surgery. I highly recommend this site: *www.plasticsurgery.org*

General Medical:

Do you need general advice about medical care? If you are looking for a website that will give good answers to important questions like: "How can I choose a doctor?"–I recommend this website: *www.kevinmd.com*.

30 Day Trial Form and Instructions

Using all your self-knowledge and self-wisdom you may want to design your own dining blueprint or compose a food strategy:

Instruction for the 30-day Trial Form: Should I try this_____? The 30-day Trial Form can be downloaded at www. amodernwomansguide.com

You may have a very good friend or even a health consultant who believes that you should be taking supplements, or vitamins, or herbs. Often, this person is very enthusiastic about their new favorite product. Or you have read about the benefits of some herb or compound. You may be interested but not totally convinced. You have read some favorable research. You are now willing to try Herb XX. Is there any way you can decide if this would benefit your health? Find your inner-scientist.

I have included in the Guide: the 30-day trial form. It *may help you evaluate the effectiveness of a vitamin or supplement on your specific physical system. It is your body - a distinctive physical system unique to you. If you wish to test a substance limit yourself to one at a time. You need to decide when and how you will ingest this pill or supplement. It is important to do it at the very same time of day, in the same manner, and consistently every day for 30 days. The first day just take the pill. The second day (before you swallow) rate the previous day on the* simple trial form. Did you feel better, worse, nothing or maybe just slightly better? Check one. If you have had a positive response for even 10 out of the 30 days, you may wish to run the trial again. Self-observation is a tool to help you decide on the value of any vitamin or supplement.

Know thy self and listen to thy self.

30-Day Trial Form

DAY	NO CHANGE	SLIGHTLY +	GREAT	WORSE
1				
2				
3				
4				
5				
6				
7				
8				
9				
10				
11				
12				
13				
14				
15				
16				
17				
18				
19				
20				
21				
22				
23				
24				
25				
26				
27				
28				
29				
30				
TOTAL				

SUBSTANCE_____

START DATE_____

Thoughts.......

Thoughts......

Thoughts……

Thoughts……

Thoughts……

Chapter 6: Road Signs:

Caution: Dangerous Curves Ahead

Humpty Dumpty sat on a wall.

Humpty Dumpty had a great fall.

All the king's horses and all the king's men

couldn't put Humpty together again!

Florence's days were easy and pleasant. They slipped by her one after the other. Her nights were warm and cozy. The three dogs kept her company, sharing her bed and her dreams.

She woke in the early morning to the dogs' insistent barking. "Out. Out. Out. " She opened the door for them, and the three of them rushed past—almost toppling her to the ground. She shuffled to the bathroom for a little pee. Florence was dressed in her favorite nightgown, the one that the children had given her two Christmases ago. She put the kettle on for tea, a proper tea with cream and honey. She might have a bowl of cereal for breakfast or not. She did not wake up with much of an appetite.

Soon the dogs were back. Knowing what was next on their morning routine, they remained at the kitchen door. They yapped with a noisy demand to be let in. Florence greeted the rowdy trio with affectionate chatter.

Every morning, Florence would give her doggie buddies a good pet and talk with them in a special high-pitched voice. "How are my loves, mumsy's darlings? Does mumsy need to feed her precious babies? Okie-dokey, loves, breakfast time, mumsy is hurrying." Florence filled their bowls generously with canned dog food. She put second dishes with doggie snacks on the floor, just in case the dears got a bit hungry.

All the animals, including the little terrier, were quite filled out, especially Lucky, the golden retriever mix. Florence adored Lucky, a large dog with a blond mane and long eyelashes. The very assertive Lucky was Florence's favorite. Lucky had become quite a puffy girl. A balloon of bark and fur.

With her pets fed and tea in hand, Florence turned on the television, and it would remain on all day. If she fell asleep in her chair, then the television would drone on all through the night, welcoming her in the morning with the first early newscast.

The telephone rang and rang. Florence finally decided to answer the annoying thing. It was her son, checking in. Florence, cranky, answered, "Oh, I am fine, just fine.... I might do a bit of weeding today.... No, I don't need a thing.... No. Nothing.... Anyway, I plan to drive myself to the grocery store—Tomorrow!... Good-bye, then."

Florence was well into her day. No need to change out of her nightgown , as she wasn't going out, and she did not expect visitors.

No need to brush her teeth. They had been spent by the time she was 75. After the last of her teeth were pulled out, the dentures had never fit well and made her gag when she wore them. She had tried to get used to them but loathed them. For a time, she would wear her dentures out for social gatherings, but now in her 80th year, she had stopped even

198

doing that. No need to comb her hair. Who would care? Certainly not the dogs. No need to wash her face—too much trouble.

Florence was not enthusiastic about showering or bathing. She had stopped bathing when she realized that she was too unsteady to get in and out of the tub, and even a shower had become a difficult and uncertain slippery chore.

Florence put her teacup in the kitchen sink, leaving her bowl of cereal on the kitchen counter.

She went into her office with its shelves of books and piles of papers.

Florence sat at her desk where she had written her last book. She turned on her computer with the intent to spend some time on Facebook. She had been an editor and researcher. She loved to argue liberal causes online. She had a firm grasp of politics and had no trouble expressing her opinions in screaming paragraphs. She wrote an earsplitting retort to a conservative Christian whose viewpoint about abortion made her indignant.

Soon, it was midday. Florence had not eaten her breakfast, so she gave it to Lucky as a special treat. Lucky eagerly lapped up the cereal and milk. When the dogs barked, she let them out into the beautiful garden that was no longer well tended, but had gone to wild exuberance and random blooms. When they scratched at the frayed doors, she brought them in again.

It was well into the afternoon. Florence had not eaten breakfast or lunch, but she was not hungry. She decided to wait to eat until dinner.

Another cup of tea, well-honeyed, would do her until then.

Evening. Dinner was put in the oven—a gourmet, frozen entrée, a nice chicken potpie. Evening—time for a glass of wine. Her pantry shelves were stocked with a liberal selection of red wine. Florence had told her daughter-in law, "I am not an alcoholic. I drink one glass of wine. Red. With my dinner."

She sat in the rocking chair on the porch looking onto the walled garden. Florence admired her climbing pink rose vine with its brave late summer flowers. She spilled some wine on her nightgown, the red stain finding plenty of company. Her glass of wine made her happy and cheerful while her dinner heated up.

She took the pie out of the oven, and let it cool awhile. Meanwhile she poured herself a second glass of wine. She took a few slurps of the pie, gumming the chicken filling a bit while spitting out the chopped vegetables. She decided she did not like the pie after all. It did not taste right. She really wasn't all that hungry. She put the remaining pie in its tin on the floor, and Lucky obligingly ate the now cold food.

She watched the evening news, hooting out loud with derision at her least favorite commentator. She was feeling really quite grand. This was her favorite time of day. She decided she could use another glass of wine. She got up from the chair with a certain effort. Her knees were a bit grouchy.

Lucky followed her to the kitchen, and that was when her legs got tangled. Was it the dog or something else? None of us will ever know. Suddenly, Florence was on the kitchen floor with her right leg at a very strange angle. Florence was now in trouble and in terrible pain. And she was unable to stand up or even sit up.

She wanted to call her son. She crawled down the hall to the guest bedroom where there was a phone, but the house was now dark, and she was confused. She twisted around on her belly and found herself wedged under the spare bed. She was turned around away from the table with the phone. She had hoped that she might have been able to pull the phone down to her. Now she was stuck and immobile. Exhausted, she lay there and remained there. Groaning. Dazed. Praying. The dogs stopped barking, doing their business on the rugs, and all three animals lay shivering in the corners of her living room.

Eventually she pissed on herself. She lay in her own urine soaked nightgown. Time passed. Forty hours later, her son and daughter-in-law came to find out why she was not answering her phone, and, perhaps more significantly, why she had stopped her tirade on Facebook.

Florence survived her fall that broke her hip. She learned to walk again, but her independent life was over.

Yes, this happened to someone I know. Do you know an older person whose life suddenly and dramatically changed? *Could this happen to you?* We are old enough to receive Social Security and a discount at the movies, but not really "old" yet. Bent over women, shuffling with a cane, with thin wisps of hair and worn expressions are the ancient ones. Not us. You and I, although not quite young, are in "late" middle age. Dear Reader, add 10 or 15 years to our age and, yes, now we are officially grazing in distant pastures. Time accelerates as the years accumulate. In 2026, I will be 80 and, darling, that ain't young.

You may have a partner. You may be one out of the three senior women who live alone. I live alone. Who will be there to help us if we fall? Who will know that we have hurt ourselves? Will you and I escape a very bad incident that changes us from an independent woman to an old lady in a nursing home? What can we do to reduce the likelihood of a tragedy? And what measures can we take to protect ourselves in case of an unwelcome emergency?

Stop here for one moment.

Contemplating an accident that will short cut our freedom and independence is frightening and depressing.

Perhaps now you would like to go back and re-read Chapters 2 through 4. Perhaps after contemplating Florence's tale, you are much more willing to make positive changes in your lifestyle and life path. This is your time and your body. I encourage you to take action to protect your vitality. Personally, I have become a serious devotee to my exercise program of weight training, swimming and yoga. I confess I still have my issues around food.

Yes, if you are fit and strong, have a reasonable diet, connection with others and purpose for staying the distance, then your chances of aging gracefully are excellent, but not certain. Yes, by self-disciplined implementation of wise choices you can definitely increase the quality of your life and lower your risks for accidents and illness.

It is true that some folks age gracefully without incident, accident or trauma. Or need for hospitalization or nursing homes. My parents,

Heinz and Beatrice, both continued righteously until for each of them a sudden medical misadventure took them quickly down and out.

Recently, I have noticed that the very self-reliant Claire, who at 50 would have never considered letting anyone else clean her house or tend her garden, has now cautiously hired occasional help. Can I expect to need more help if I live another 10 or 20 years? You bet I will.

You may age very well and need only a cleaning lady and a good hair cut to finish your years in society. *But, what if...?*

THIS IS IMPORTANT: Now, when you are well and clear of mind, is the time to consider preparations for an unplanned illness or accident.

Experts in the field of the aging population have come up with an evaluation of a person's ability to manage on their own. This is referred to as the ADL or **A**ctivities of **D**aily **L**iving:

The list seems minimal to me. It is the bare bones for staying out of a home for the infirm.

Bathing

Dressing and undressing

Eating

Transferring from bed to chair, and back

Voluntary control of urinary and fecal discharge

Using the toilet

Walking (not bedridden)

The guideline suggests that if a person wishes to live on their own in their own residence, it would be great if she could also accomplish other tasks such as:

Light housework

Preparing meals

Taking medications

Shopping for groceries or clothes

Using the telephone

Managing money

These formal guidelines seem rather limited and bleak. For me, my zest-filled life has to include the ability to create art, read, write, exercise, travel and entertain friends. I also want to be able to dance like a wild child, manipulate small jewelry tools, be curious about the world and be open to change. This is how I am feeling right now, but I acknowledge I may change my opinion, as I get older. Or not.

I can give up driving my car, downhill skiing, and skydiving, and still think of myself as vital.

Does this mean that if I cannot do everything on my "got to" list that I will want to die? Immediately? I need to seriously think about this. What can I give up or give in to, and still feel positive about being alive? What do you think are the main criteria that would allow you to exist in the manner that makes you glad to be alive? Excuse me, Claire, I am too young to contemplate this issue. Maybe, maybe not.

List the ten things that make your life definitely worth living. Just use a random piece of paper, the form at the end of the chapter, or download the form. What is on your list? Nice job, but really—Mahjong?

So what would make life untenable for you? Can you name your biggest fears?

For me:

1. Peeing and pooping in my pants.

2. Being unable to see.

3. Being unable to walk unassisted.

4. Being unable to manage my own money.

5. Being unable to feed myself.

No, I am not going to change my mind about these five.

Take your time and name five circumstances that would seriously fray the fabric of your good life. Think about it. Review your answers. Did you write a list on a piece of paper?

It is a scary list. Set a match to the piece of paper and let the fumes reach the heavens as prayer. Don't burn your fingers. I never want any of those things to happen to any of my readers or to myself.

Let us continue to work on staying healthy and strong. Let us savor the here and now. We are older women making excellent choices. We have done everything to stay vital and alert.

However, *something could go terribly wrong*. What would happen if you had a stroke, a car accident, or like Florence, broke your hip? After you were rescued, you might be in such poor shape that you could not communicate or in any way supervise your care.

What happened to Florence after she was found?

Florence was taken to the hospital by ambulance. It was clear she did have Medicare and a supplementary plan. For a while, no one knew if she had a drug plan. Florence had spent 40 hours lying injured on a hard floor without water or food. She was suffering from shock. For two days she could not answer simple questions. As it turned out, she had signed up for a supplementary drug plan, but she was three months in arrears. Her family was able to pay the back amount owed and reinstate her drug plan. Whew!

She had been paying her electric, but not her phone bill. Her gas bill was current, but the heating system was not working properly. She had been buying expensive dog food, but her pantry was bare of nourishing food for herself.

What can we learn from Florence's experience? To start with:

- Consider putting all your bills on automatic withdrawal from your bank account.

- Consider having a friend or relative check in with you every day.

- Consider evaluating your home for its safety.

What do you have in place that will help your rescuers, faithful friends or innocent family members to take charge while you are out of commission?

Those of us who are setting such plans in motion, we could think of our efforts as good manners. We are being considerate of our saviors who may themselves be quite upset and distraught. Put yourself in their place. Wouldn't you want instructions and guidelines?

You find yourself muttering, "I really do not want anyone to know my business. I do not like the idea of someone having this kind of access to my life."

The hard truth: *One day you will be gone.* Someone you love or just someone will look through all your personal papers, clothing, jewelry, and flotsam and jetsam. Your stuff will be either be thrown away, given away, put in a museum (an artist's dream) or hopefully cherished by another person. Somebody may fight with somebody else over Grandma's ring. *Everybody will want your money and your house.*

When I had to deal with my mother's belongings, I was grateful she was such an orderly person. She died in Manhattan and I live in the

Southwest. My two daughters, Melissa (beautiful, tall and blonde) and Vanessa (beautiful, tall and brunette) flew to New York to help me sort it out. My girls, in their early twenties, were capable energetic young women. I decided we had three choices in our method of coping with all her furniture, clothing, art and household goods. Things went to charity, Pinky's students and friends as commemorative gifts, or were sent to my home in a moving van. My mother was not a hoarder—she disliked anything extraneous. Everything in her apartment was neatly arranged. She was very deliberate. She disliked clutter. All her possessions were elegant and tasteful. We hardly threw anything away. *Thanks, Pinky.*

Have you had a family member kick the bucket (quaint euphemism)? Did you have to delve into their life? How about yourself? Got any mystery corners you would not like anyone to find?

Are you prepared for the scrutiny of another person? You might consider lightening the load, sorting through your belongings, and keeping the essentials.

For a moment, just think how would you feel if you were the person who had to deal with your junk. You may decide that if you are gone, then it is not your problem. You do not care. The big *'So what?'*. Or now that you have thought about it, maybe you will destroy the erotic photographs of you and your old lover. Or frame them?

Are you ready to set up a system so that concerned people can handle a serious event that leaves you incapacitated? Suggestion: An unlocked metal box labeled HELP FOR MY HELPERS or IN THE EVENT OF AN EMERGENCY that is easily seen and located. Just where did you put the box? Leave a small printed note on the refrigerator and/or tell the location to the right person. If you locked the box, then "where is the key?" or "what in god's name is the combination?" becomes another logistical obstacle for your friends to overcome to provide you with assistance.

I purchased a steel box (online has quite a few selections) that had file compartments and then I set up an easy to access system. I put duct tape over my steel fireproof chest, just so only the serious need enquire.

What could you put in your container? Medical directives, insurance information, a simple map of how to run your life, your will or living trust, possibly a list of assets, if I die—what to do, where you hid the big wad of cash, a tasteless joke, and maybe some kind words to those you love.

Inspired, now you now have a beautiful fireproof metal box. Your metal box is unlocked and has written on it in clear letters: **HELP FOR MY HELPERS.** Let us earnestly consider what you might include as useful information, for concerned persons, in case of an emergency that we all hope will never happen:

1. <u>**HOW TO ACCESS MY LIFE**</u>**—Medical and related information**: One of the most important documents that you can provide is an advance care document, living will or durable power of attorney for health care. The purpose of this document is to assign responsibility to one person who can make decisions about your medical care if you are

unable to do so. Do your best to select someone you can trust, who will stay calm in times of trouble and who will agree to respect your instructions. There is a comprehensive kit (which you can download for free) called the "Five Wishes" which covers these important issues and gives you an opportunity to get very specific about how you want to be treated. "Five Wishes" is legal in most states—if properly witnessed or notarized. You just might want to fill it out, have it witnessed and throw it in the box. Another copy could be filed with your doctor and another given to your executor. Medical insurance information might consist of copies of your social security card, medical insurance card and any supplementary plans you are covered by. The name of your primary doctor might be useful. Include real, detailed instructions. For instance, "I can be put on a ventilator or an induced coma for a short term, if I am not brain dead, as a temporary measure if there is a good likelihood of recovery." Be as specific as you can be.

2. <u>TO RUN MY HOME</u>—**A map of how your life is managed:** You would like things to run smoothly while you are ill. It would be nice to come home and have the lights working. The cat alive. Even the plants blooming. If your mortgage is not paid up, how do you pay for your shelter? Utilities, how are they paid? Your credit cards—how are they managed? Include a copy of the face and back of your cards. Let us get really personal. How do you get the money you live on? Tell us so we can continue paying for things. Does your money derive from Social Security payments, pensions, annuities, IRAs, checking accounts, robbing banks, your business or a salary? Can someone nearby sign your checks to pay your bills? Do you

210

have outstanding debts or loans? Yes, you might have to update this once a year. On April Fool's Day? May Day?

3. <u>IN CASE OF DEATH:</u> If you have climbed the stairway to heaven, who gets what? A document that covers distributing your goods and assets is called a *will*. When you make a will, you also have to choose an executor who takes the will to probate court. Yes, this can be the same person to whom you have assigned the medical decision-making, if you like. As you know from reading mystery novels, the will can be changed any time, and if witnessed properly the most recent one is the only one regarded as valid. If you forget to write a will and have a substantive negative outcome (awkward euphemism for death), then the state will have to make choices for you. You may have set up a *revocable living trust* to bypass the probate court. Now your son who needs all the help he can get is empowered to immediately move into your house and ruin your decorating scheme. You have deprived your local judiciary system of future income while enhancing the budget of your local estate lawyer.

Do you have life insurance? Where are the policies? Do you have a ***safety deposit box***? Where is it? Where is the key?

Your will can include explicit instructions about distributing your belongings. Pets? What about the African grey parrot, Sheila? Were you aware that she has a life expectancy of 73 years? Yes, you should include bequests for the treatment of surviving animals.

4. <u>**WHAT I WANT YOU TO DO WITH MY MORTAL REMAINS:**</u> If there is a body (you did not expire in a plane crash, tsunami

or a fire), what exactly do you want done with your remains?

How to cope with the leftover human corpse is often culturally determined. A modern woman may have innovative ideas about disposing of her cadaver. There is often a hefty price tag. You can buy a small life insurance policy. You can leave a cash sum for the purpose of defraying these expenses.

Popular choices for dealing with the body:

Cremation uses high temperature heat to reduce the body to a modest amount of dry crumbly bits. The average cost of this treatment is over $1,000. Next you have to decide what to do with those remaining bits. You might leave instructions, "I want my daughters to throw my ashes in the Nile, and I have included in my estate two first-class round-trip tickets to Egypt." Or you might include in your last thoughts, "Put my ashes in a Ming dynasty urn. Bury the urn with a headstone in the family plot. Inscribe the headstone: *'We all loved her very much.'* Place me next to my deceased first husband, not your dead father."

Recently, I discovered a biodegradable vessel (*urnabios.com*) that you can put ashes in, bury, and then have a tree planted over the container. There is no tombstone as lovely as a tree.

Burial: You can request to be buried in a casket in a cemetery. An average price is more than $2,000 for a metal, wood, fiberboard or plastic model. The casket is the single most expensive item in a traditional funeral. Mahogany, bronze or copper models run up to $10,000 or more. Burial

212

plots in a cemetery cost between $1000 to $4500. Price tags everywhere. The cost to dig the hole to put the casket in could be $800. Headstones cost between $400 and $1700. Your obituary in the local paper is not free. This is certainly starting to add up. *The Social Security Administration will give your family $255 to defray burial expenses.* Thanks so much. While you are alive, consider buying a burial plot for yourself. Yes, you might very well want to leave a special fund to cover these expenses. You might consider some kind of paid up or regular life insurance to manage the cost of saying good-bye. I know I am repeating myself.

I am thinking of creating my own casket with the surface painted with scenes from my life. Colorful. Maybe this winter.

What if you want your body wrapped in a linen shroud and placed in a hole in the ground on private property? Food for the worms. The ultimate in biodegradable. You may need to check on your local ordinances. What will they permit you to do? You might want a simple headstone to mark the place. Nice to warn the utility company. Leave clues for future archeologists. *"Her body became earth. Her soul, sky."* If your local laws allow, this could be a low-cost burial.

You might leave your body to **medical science** *(medcure.org)*. Consider donating some of your organs. They might be useful to another person now that you have left the theater. This can be noted on your driver's license.

You could choose **cryonics,** the practice or technique of deep-freezing your body after death. You could leave this cryptic note: "I am a member of Alcor (a company specializing in cryonics) in good standing. You will find here a $200,000 life insurance policy with Alcor (*alcor.org*) as the beneficiary. This arrangement will allow my body to be kept frozen until science discovers a way to bring me back. My cells are being preserved until science can clone me. I have set up a special fund. Consult my lawyer, Ms. Jarndyce. Next time, I am to be raised Catholic."

5. CELEBRATE ME–What should the funeral or memorial look like? How would you like your life celebrated? Leave instructions, and if possible, money. My husband, Michael, had a heart condition that was obviously terminal. We all knew for a year that he soon would be released from his failing body. Our daughters talked to him about his wishes. Michael wanted a gathering of friends, food and conversation. And then dancing to his favorite music, Motown from the sixties. After he died, we did what he had asked of us. His memorial was a gathering of hundreds of people followed by words, singing, potluck, and music. We live in an unconventional artist colony. A caring, small town. My children set up a display of tear-inducing photographs. I found myself dancing until late evening. I know Michael would have enjoyed the gathering. He was only 57 when he abandoned his ever so handsome vessel. We had his discarded body cremated. I released his ashes in the Rio Grande River. I had instructions and did my best to follow them.

6. LAST CHANCE: Do you have some very important things that need to be said? Do you need to say something to someone? Loving words could be very healing. A secret that needs telling? It would be good for you

214

to write it down.

Are you finding all of this very depressing? Some humor—Joan Rivers: "You know you're getting old when you buy a sexy sheer nightgown and don't know anyone who can see through it." Robin Williams: "Death is nature's way of saying, 'Your table's ready.'" Woody Allen: "It's not that I'm afraid to die, I just don't want to be there when it happens."

7. <u>ODDS AND ENDS</u>: Who needs to be informed? List the names and the contact information of people who should know what has happened to you. You might want to include some easily understood instructions where cash or other notables are located. Have you a charitable endowment that no one knows about? You could write a last statement to be read at your funeral. You could write your own obituary. Please do whatever would make you feel satisfied with your final arrangements. Here is a poem that I have included in my own odds and ends folder.

Addendum: Instructions to be Attached to My Will

I want to die
in full command
of my brain/ my bowels/ my bladder

After:
I would like you to gather and say a few words-
Words: razors/tough/honest
No sweet lies.
Save the sugar.

Praise my cooking.
My Thanksgiving Turkey—
the Greatest:
no contest.

Now:
Laugh.
My snoring, my posture,
my driving –
I do not care. I cannot hear.

Balance with:
You could not fool her....
A nice smile.
A fine artist.
Whatever seems truest.

Give away the furniture.
Burn the writings.
Water the plants.
Just throw out all my clothes–
out of style.

Daughters, grandchildren
Did you find the cash?
Share the money. Fly to Paris.

Say I was . . . different/special/ ridiculous.
I never knew how to beautifully wrap
the gifts I spent so much time choosing.
Take the best of me.
You cannot escape–I dance in your DNA.

Put important keys and passwords in one envelope. The envelope can say, "You might need this!" Can you think of anything else that would support the people who are trying to help you?

It might be helpful to communicate to a family member or friend where this thrilling repository is stored or even thoroughly discuss the contents before anything happens. Maybe nothing that warrants these efforts will ever occur; still this information is wise to put together. Maybe you will pass away sitting on the porch watching the sunset over the pond while listening to Pachelbel Canon in D Major.

Or maybe you will be like many sad cases and end up in an old folks' home for 18 months, before expiring in a badly furnished room with a vase of wilted flowers on your nightstand.

Part of the really dreadful news is that this woeful ending is very expensive, costing anywhere from $4000 to $12,000 dollars **a month**. This is one more subject where my research makes me want to short-circuit the process.

For so many families, the lifetime savings that were meant to buy a new home for the not-so-young daughter or to send a grandchild to college will be spent keeping Grandma preserved in a room fragrant with the odors of death.

My friend Carolyn told me that her daddy spent 14 months in a nursing home at the New York cost of $10,000 a month. The family spent all of his tenderly collected assets of a modest lifetime on a few months of care. After he died, she and her two sisters each inherited $600.

What if you have enough financial clout to buy into a Senior Complex that has provisions for various stages of aging, including assisted living and end-of-life care? If you can afford it, and it appeals to you, then it could be an excellent solution. This could be an expensive choice, but the troublesome issue is nicely resolved.

If you are truly poor and have very few assets or you use up all your equity, then Medicaid will pay for your nursing home, but you may not like their choice of a place. Warning: Giving away everything you own is clever, but you are not the first to think of it. Old timers' storage facilities will look back seven years to check on how you have disposed of your possessions. They really want you to pay for your special time at their establishment.

You may be able to buy insurance for long-term care. This is expensive insurance. I am considering applying for a policy. I can be insured for Home Care, Assisted Living and Nursing Home Care. The company will cover my costs of up to $5000 a month for up to four years (not forever). I will have to pay $370 a month, with a $4000 deductible, and the provider is very careful about who they will insure. In other words, no matter at what age I take out a policy, I cannot have a pre-existing health condition. I cannot have ever smoked, had a recent surgery or have heart disease. A medical professional will carefully examine me to see if I am healthy enough for them to take a risk. It remains to be seen if I can even qualify for this plan.

And you can die in the hospital (a common American choice). Dying in a hospital, festively decorated with tubes and on a ventilator, would be covered by your insurance. Or, if your doctor can establish that you have less than six months to live, Medicaid will pay for hospice care. Hospice may serve you or a loved one as a compassionate and good ending. More people and their families are accepting that a gentle, supported death with appropriate palliative care is the best choice for all concerned. Peaceful.

Remember Florence and her great fall? Yes, she went by ambulance to the local hospital. After surgery on her broken hip and a weeklong hospital stay, Florence spent six weeks in a nursing home/ rehabilitation facility. Florence found herself in the company of the very elderly and the very broken down. Most of the residents were in wheel-chairs or bedridden. Very few of them had much to say. The staff loved her irascible personality and took great interest in their very intelligent patient. The staff provided consistent physical therapy and dedicated care. Florence has a strong will. Florence got out of bed and up on her shaking legs. After a couple of weeks she could use the bathroom on her own. Medicare paid for this interim care, and she could have stayed in this facility for the full hundred days, but she really wanted to get the hell out of there.

Before Florence could return to her house, a health social worker analyzed the safety of her environment and made recommendations for refitting the place to meet the needs of a senior woman. Here are some of the changes that were made:

- Entryway ramps to accommodate her less mobile state

- Bathroom safety grip bars and a walk-in shower

- Medical alert system

- Lever style door and sink handles

- Improved lighting and night lighting

- Handrails

- Removal of scatter rugs and some furniture

- Improved pathways in the house

Before life dictates radical changes, could you make your house more accident-proof?

Florence got to go back home. Her house had a small apartment attached to it, which could provide a residence for a full-time caregiver. Sylvia was happy to be hired to watch over Florence. She was compensated with a monthly salary and her own place to live. Sylvia is an agreeable, middle-aged lady, who likes to keep a tidy house and is a good cook.

Florence can live at home as long as there is some one to check on her several times each day. She is supervised when she bathes. Her meals are cooked for her, her laundry is done, and her house kept clean. The sun is shining.

Lucky (the dog) met an untimely end in the form of canine stomach cancer. Florence wept. Florence still lives and sleeps with the two remaining pooches. Florence enjoys her evening glass of red wine. Her son took over her checkbook. She no longer drives her green Buick. She spends time on Facebook every day. Florence would tell you that she is very happy.

Continuing the Conversation

Suggested Readings:

Hope I Don't Die Before I Get Old: How to Survive Old Age, Your Own or Someone You Love written by Tracey Bowman and Mary Boone Wellington, published by Rose Cottage Publishing.

Two bright, caring women who have aging parents share their experiences. They both have parents who have reached an end to their ability to live independently. We walk with them through the struggles and crises as well as the good solutions and inevitable farewells. As well as engaging us in their personal sagas, the ladies include valuable information and guidance on handling end-of-life situations. This book is mix of "what happened to Mom on the way to the funeral parlor" and injections of helpful information on dealing with aging issues.

Preparing for the Inevitable: A Practical Guide for Dealing with End-of-Life Issues written by Peter Callan, published by Watermelon Productions.

This is short and sweet and to the point. Included are documents you can use to do the job of self-preparation for the conclusion of your life. P.S. *Prepare to Die* (another title for the same pamphlet) is a good tool.

Eldercare for Dummies written by Rachelle Sukerman, PhD., published by Wiley Productions.

This book contains friendly practical advice written in simple, clear language. The purpose of this guide is to help you take excellent care of your elderly relatives. Of course, you can easily apply the information in this book to—yourself. Very well organized.

__The 9 Steps to Financial Freedom: Practical & Spiritual Steps So You Can Stop Worrying__ written by Suze Orman, published by Three Rivers Press.

Money, just like sex and death, is often a taboo subject. This excellent book can help you make decisions about your finances.

Useful Websites:

__www.amodernwomansguide.com__

You can go to my website to download any journals or forms that I have included in the guide. I will share anything new I learn about navigating aging and end-of-life planning with frequent updates and thoughts.

Thoughtful ways to consider dealing with your body post-life:

__Green ways of dealing with death:__

Bios Urn turns death into a transformation and a return to life through nature. The Bios Urn is a fully biodegradable urn designed to convert you into a tree after life. Mainly composed of two parts, the urn contains a seed, which will grow into a tree. You can choose your favorite tree. I chose Beech.

Check out: *urnabios.com*

Donating Organs: When you have breathed your last breath (after death), you may wish to donate your body to science or have your no longer needed body parts made available to help the living.

Go to *www.organdonor.gov*

222

**Life after death:** If you are searching for a way to have life after death, and you are not talking about reincarnation, then you might want to contact the Alcor Life Extension Foundation. We are talking _**cryonics**_ (the practice or technique of deep-freezing the bodies of those who have died of an incurable disease, in the hope of a future cure). Very cold. Brrr. "Alcor intervenes in the dying process as soon as possible **after** legal **death** to preserve the brain as well as possible."

A very expensive service: _www.alcor.org_

Here is an agreeable site that keeps up to date on the latest thinking about funerals, burials etc., in a very neutral, conscientious fashion.

Visit: _www.treehugger.com_

You may want to evaluate your home for its risks before, not after....

This is a great website. I recommend you use the Home Safety Self Assessment Tool. **HSSAT** is designed to help you analyze which areas in your home are potential accidents just waiting to happen. This assessment tool includes drawings. Their clear visual aids specifically address individual rooms and outdoor spaces of your home.
Visit: _agingresearch.buffalo.edu_

One site that has everything (and more) about end-of-life preparation:

Here is a one-stop shop. This elaborate site is full of practical information, articles about how to plan for death and important forms. All you might need or wish to know about preparing for death and dying.

I recommend: _DeathWise.org._

Considering our quality of life: What makes your life worth living?

YOUR JOURNAL FOR SELF-UNDERSTANDING:

List ten things that make your life definitely worth living.
And put a star* by the three that are the most important to you.

What makes your existence enjoyable and meaningful? Really, what is essential to making your life pleasurable? You might find there are very few things that make your list. Or you may need more room.

1._____

2._____

3._____

4._____

5._____

6._____

7._____

8._____

9._____

10._____

So, now you can savor the wonderful things that make your life great.

Take a moment to turn over the rock. *Can you name five conditions that would seriously fray the fabric of your good life?* What situations or physical changes would severely diminish your quality of life?

1._____

2._____

3._____

4._____

5._____

Do you think you could make the necessary adjustment to your changed circumstances? If any of these conditions or situations occurred, would you still want to continue living?

Thoughts…….

Thoughts......

Thoughts…….

Thoughts…...

Thoughts…...

Chapter Seven: The Last Laugh and

Other Thoughts on Dying

Death governs everything—trees, bees, worms, elephants, solar systems, and every woman that inhabits a temporary, meant-to-self-destruct body. This is the given: your life is an unknown amount of time between the bookends of your birth and your death.

When I was young, I was immortal. As I age, I have been thinking much more about my demise and its effect on the family I leave behind, who I hope will be alive to witness my departure and inherit the material goods I have accumulated from a successful career.

I, Claire Haye, wish to exit gently and to leave behind tidiness and generosity—a clear message from me that I cared.

I can accept the fact that my life will close. It is the truth. My certain ending is the last sentence in the last chapter: Claire Haye: b. March 27, 1946, Chicago, Ill. d. _____, ___ ,_____,____.

As an older woman and a widow, I have suffered the loss of members of my own family.

I was with my mother, Pinky, when she died. She passed away in her own bed, in her elegant apartment just where and how she wanted.

Really? Oh, how I wish it had been that simple.

It was the spring of 1995. I was in New Mexico, and she was in New York. Far apart from my mother, yet I sensed her—fragile and tenuous. I told my husband Michael, "My mother is dying—I just know it."

I got on a plane and flew across the country to see her. I arrived in Manhattan late Friday evening, April 28th, 1995. I took a cab to her apartment building.

The doorman rang me up, and when I got off the elevator, my mother was standing in the open doorway. We held each other.

Long distance I had known my mother was fading. Holding her I was shocked by the reality.

My mother, "Darling, you must be starving. Airplane food is so awful. I went out with a friend for Chinese. I couldn't eat it all. I brought some home for you."

I looked at my mother. Pinched, dull, indefinably wrong. I thought, "Oh my god, she is in serious trouble."

My luggage and I dragged into her apartment. I sat down on the hard narrow modern couch. Mom brought me a plateful of warmed-up food.

I asked her, "What in the hell is wrong with you?"

She said, "I am not feeling well. I am dizzy. My vision is blurred, and sometimes everything just goes dark."

She was a few weeks shy of her 85th birthday. My mother, formerly known as the modern dancer Beatrice Von Stronstorff, still taught her long-time pupils in the studio in her apartment. For many years, she had been the movement guru to a wild assortment of musicians, opera singers, and painters. For the last few years, she had also been working at a theater school, The New Actors Workshop. My mother taught improvisational movement to group of young, would-be thespians. In five years she had never missed a class. The theater students adored their coach, their diva. Bea.

Bea—aka Beatrice, aka Pinky, aka Grandma B., aka Mom—at 84 was still working Monday through Saturday. She also took proper care of herself, her apartment and her finances. She knew her own mind.

Her generation was dying. After happening upon an obituary of a long-ago flame, she mourned, "Now, every man who ever loved me is dead."

Pinky was the only one still living of her original family of six siblings. She was the baby of the family. Pauline, her favorite sister, had succumbed 15 months before.

Over the last few years, I'd had several chats with Mom on the topic of her dying.

Pinky: "I want to die teaching one of my students. He finishes his exercises, looks around and finds me in my chair." She was probably hoping "he" would be Sandy, the opera singer, one of her most beloved pupils. And Sandy might have thought it an honor.

In the summer of 1993, my mother and I had taken the train from Manhattan to Connecticut to visit her 92-year old sister, Pauline. My aunt was still living in her house with its well-tended grounds. Pauline had spent decades in Japan. Before she retired, she had managed an Asian

Import Company with offices in Manhattan.

Over the years, she had transformed her Connecticut yard into a serene Japanese garden. We arrived at her house. Aunt Pauline was no longer the woman we had known. She had full-time caretakers. Pauline was outside being pushed in her wheelchair by a helper. My aunt was bent over in the chair. Her head twisted and crooked like an inquisitive bird. She was drooling on her robe.

My wonderful, brilliant aunt who used to whip out her fountain pen and kill the New York Times crossword puzzle. Twenty minutes, no more. Aunt Pauline spoke, but we did not understand her words.

My mother in a tight quiet voice, "If you see me like that, I want you to smother me with a pillow. Just put a pillow over my head. You understand?"

I had listened carefully to my mother's thoughts about her death, but I did not expect to be present at her last moments. Yes, my mother had clearly communicated to me how she felt about losing her ability to function and run her own life. I had journeyed from New Mexico to her New York apartment because I was concerned about her. Here and now my mother and I were together, and I was not sure what to do.

It was Saturday morning, April 29th, 1995. I had spent a restless night attempting to sleep on the futon in my mother's office. When morning finally arrived, I phoned my children. Vanessa (the younger) said, "We will bring Grandma B. to our home and take care of her." Melissa (the first born) asked, "How are *you* doing, Mom?"

I convinced my mother to call her physician. I listened to her side of the conversation. She yelled in the phone, "No, I do not want to go the Emergency Room of the hospital. No, I will not meet you there.... All right, all right, I will come into the office first thing on Monday."

I conferred with our cousin Larry, a well-known psychiatrist. He had his colleague—a big-name neurologist—phone the house. This doctor asked if she had been taking her blood pressure medicine.

Pinky responded, "No, I ran out of pills and haven't had the prescription refilled."

The neurologist begged me to bring her to the hospital. Pinky declined.

April 30th, 1995 was the last Sunday. Pinky got up and made her usual pot of very strong coffee. The smell of brewing coffee brought me to the kitchen. There she was. My mother stood hunched over, in a white lacy nightgown, her dark hair lank around her. Unsteady. She held her hand against the kitchen wall. She said, "It is so strange, I haven't put on my makeup this morning."

Later that morning, two sisters, her devoted students, came by with her blood pressure medicine and also with a cuff to find out how she was doing. 240/160.

I made everybody Sunday brunch. My mother sat with us for a while. Then she excused herself and went to bed.

When our visitors left, my mother and I had this conversation:

Mom: "What do you think is wrong with me?"

Me: "You are having a series of strokes."

Mom: "What is the worst that can happen?"

Me: "You will die."

Mom: "I am ready to embrace death."

What followed is really hard to share. I kept asking her to go to the hospital, and she kept rebuffing me.

Late that Sunday evening, I said, "Mom, *please* let us go to the hospital. I want to take you."

She said to me in a clear, loud, and very firm voice, "I absolutely refuse to go to the hospital." And that was the last thing my mother ever said to me. It was my loneliest night. Nightmares when I did fall asleep.

The phone rang very early Monday morning, May 1st. It was a call from my older daughter.

Me: "She isn't good; I think she is in a coma."

Melissa firmly: "You have to call an ambulance."

I called 911. By the time the ambulance came she was gone. The paramedics, finding her dead, quickly applied a defibrillator to her naked chest. Reminiscent of a cattle prod. They shocked her chest again and again. Her heart began to beat. The paramedics were pleased. They were doing their job. If she could have, she would have told them, "I absolutely forbid you to touch me."

I became hysterical. Panicked. The year before she had signed and notarized a "Do Not Resuscitate" order. I felt dizzy. Crazy. I found the document shoved at the back of a shelf in her closet. I showed it to the paramedics. The guys, shaking their heads, told me, "Nah... This piece of paper won't work. You have the wrong form.... This thing ain't legal in

New York State."

They put her on a stretcher and took her by ambulance to the hospital.

That evening, Monday May 1st, 1995, in spite of all the hospital's efforts, Pinky died again. And the medical community allowed her to rest in peace. R.I.P.

Is this a horror story? Or does it have a happy ending? Should I have been put in jail? What would you have done?

Again. What have you put in place to inform your family or an interested person during a crisis? Is this information easy for someone to find? Consider re-reading Chapter 6. Consider actually putting in place the recommendations in Chapter 6.

Let us say that I have done all I can possibly do to be gracious in dire circumstances. Signed every document. Written clear instructions. Put all the paper work in the fireproof metal box. The box is easy to locate. Tidied all the closets. Thrown out my old boyfriend's love letters. Framed my nude photographs. Informed the children what to do with my corpse. Left a map and a working key to the buried treasure.

I have done everything I need to do. I can put the entire issue of being prepared and considerate aside.

I am still left with the profound issue of facing my own death.

Nature's unsentimental message is clear: "Move on. You have had many years on earth, and soon it will be time to depart and make room for the next generation." And I say, I "get it", but it is me (ME) that you are asking to leave.

The big truth: It does not matter how well we have monitored our health, thought positive thoughts, successfully modified the appearance of aging, exercised appropriately, taken special supplements, disciplined ourselves around food, or embraced a meaningful life. We will depart this place. We will cease. How comfortable are you with the reality of your own limited time? Your own finite existence?

As for myself, I am not so much afraid of dying, as I am afraid of deteriorating to the point that I have lost control of my life. What worries me is the transition between the healthy older woman and a frail old woman. May my passing be mercifully gentle and quick!

Unfortunately, there is no guarantee of a smooth exit from a body that has been my home for generations. What if I just keep getting older and older, and I end up so old that even I do not know how old I am?

Senescence is the final stage of the normal life span. How will I recognize that I am in *senescence*? Will I be able to say, with some self-authority, "I am definitely done dancing"?

The big uncertainty is how I can handle, manage, and even enhance my own dying process.

In a society that has a large population of old-old fogies, how profound would it be if we, the elders, were to embrace a serious contemplation of the end time and show the young how to do it—with dignity, intelligence, and compassion?

And what about the generations of people who will be here after we die off? What kind of disaster am I handing over to my grandchildren and their children?

I spend more time with my family at Christmas than I do at any other time of year. The holiday season is very charming in a small town. Melissa (my daughter), her husband Alex, their teenage sons, and I went to a huge everybody-is-invited party. My friend Mark was also at this gathering. Accompanying Mark was his getting-on-in-years mother Ellen.

Ellen was seated at the dining room table with a plateful of holiday food. Her head barely came over the level of the wood table. She smiled. Her false teeth shone bright and white. Her stiff dyed hair was a tight helmet around her tiny wrinkled face. Her eyes were animated and alive behind large tortoise-rimmed glasses. Today was her 99th birthday. "Happy Birthday!" We sang loudly and of course off-key. Ellen smiled. And there was cake. One candle.

My grandson, Niko, looked at me in a very affectionate way, and said the most amazing thing, "Gramma, I hope you live to be 99." I hope not.

Why? Here is the problem facing all of us: My generation, the boomers, are going to live too long.

There is a shark in the swimming pool—a looming prospect of a huge community of over-80 seniors. In poor health, low vitality, and needing a myriad of services. Who will provide these services? Who will pay for them? Society will be heavily burdened by an aging population. This will be a society out of balance. The distortion of the population growth of older folk vs. the sector of younger, healthy, able-bodied workers is frightening.

A quick look into the future: We are in the year 2045. I have celebrated my 99th birthday. Niko (my dear grandson), at 49, has finally paid off his student loans. He has opened his own financial consultant office. Last year, after multiple prenuptials were signed, he and his partner got married in Fiji. Lawyers in love. His 45-year-old wife, Madison, has announced she is pregnant with triplets. Girls. Just last week, they bought their dream condo in Chicago with a view of the lake.

The government has announced yet another bonus program to entice young people to immigrate to the states from Mexico and South America. "Come and work in the USA. We guarantee a bonus of $10,000 after your first year of employment. Citizenship with full rights after two years." What else? Niko's tax rate has been raised to a record 55 percent of his adjusted income. What else? His health insurance rates have doubled. Again. Yes, the children will be quite a tax shelter. The high tax bills, the elevated insurance rates, the crowded streets, the cost of water, the summer heat, and the waiting lists for apartments. Maybe Niko won't mind or won't notice. Maybe.

If I am alive at 99, will I want to be in this world? I would be curious about my triplet great-granddaughters. I might want to meet them. Hold them. One at a time. Really, it is not enough. I can imagine myself very, very tired of living in a body that has definitely passed its prime.

Will I have found a new art form that engages me? Be in love? With a man my age? Will I still be able to swim or even get up from a chair? Many of us may want to leave the building while we can still walk out the exit door. Even without a major health crisis, I may not want to continue.

If we contemplate the beginning and the ending of life, we might agree that:

Birth is welcomed with joy and celebration—tears of happiness.

Death receives formal and solemn ceremony—tears of grief.

Can we imagine a joyful, celebratory death? Can we imagine designing a final ceremony that includes stories, farewells, laughter, gifts, and a delicious meal? A grand occasion or quiet gathering that we planned while we were alive. A special event that we attend in spirit only.

Or do we want a *farewell* supper, a last gathering that we do attend as a physical person? How could we manage the timing of this very unusual event? Could we be strong enough to be there? Maybe we should have an annual goodbye and I love-you-all event every year we live past 80. Champagne, but definitely no balloons.

It may seem like an unrealistic dream to be so reconciled to and aware of your own death that you could host a party for yourself. **It takes a new cultural imagination.** I believe that it is time to work on remaking our attitude towards death. I am sure we can create alternate views of this life event. To help you begin the process, you can find after this chapter (or at *amodernwomansguide.com*), an exercise to share with a small group of friends entitled "*A Lunch with Meaning –Writing Your Own Obituary*". Fun! Are you kidding? Surprisingly, all the participants generally have a lovely afternoon.

How do I feel about my own death? I want to meet my end time with acceptance and a tender smile. I am going to invent my own last celebration. I have left a short statement to be read at my memorial. Honestly,

I cannot predict my own decline or how I will feel as death reaches for my hand, but I will hold the thought that I can consciously open the gate.

You may decide an old-fashioned and very unplanned death is the way to go. You may feel that life in *any form* with *any amount of pain* is worth staying for. Your spiritual or religious beliefs may ensure that you will go the distance no matter the cost to yourself, your family, or your society. I understand that this is a clear and powerful desire on your part. I do not share the same reality.

Living beings are born with the will to survive. As a thinking person I might decide it was time to be released from my physical body, but I might find it impossible to actually figure out how.

Would I be willing or able to take myself out if I was utterly miserable? What if I was unable to see that my situation would ever improve? Suicide. Deliberately ending your own life. Shocking! What a thought. Your principles may make it unlikely that you would ever contemplate such a solution.

Here we are. This is a tightrope moment. We are walking a thin wire across a mountain pass. Far beneath are roaring rapids and sharp rocks. Hand me my magic long pole. Balance.

Could I exit when I decide my time is up without creating a traumatic event for my family? If I decided to stage my own death, what would be the best method? Truthfully, I do not have any answers. Yet. Even if I am unable to answer these questions for myself, *I can view with compassion and acceptance another woman's choice.*

244

Doing the research for this book, I quickly learned that there is a worldwide movement promoting *death with dignity*. There is deep curiosity, a longing to know, and willingness to shine a light on the subject. Not surprisingly, many of the pioneers of this movement themselves experienced the loss of someone they loved very much. A precious someone they loved who died from a terrible painful illness.

A BRIEF HISTORY OF THE RIGHT TO CHOOSE TO DIE WHEN YOU THINK IT IS TIME:

Derek Humphry was happily married to Jean. She became very ill with terminal breast cancer. Derek and Jean decided that she did not want to continue suffering. Her last cup of coffee was laced with sleeping pills and painkillers provided by a sympathetic doctor. Cream or sugar? Actually she took milk. She died gently at home.

Three years later, Derek, a journalist, wrote a memoir of their experience. Brave. *Jean's Way–A Love Story* was published in 1978 and is still in print today. If you read it, you will understand. Derek's actions made him an accessory to a death, a felony. After the book was published, detectives were alerted to his crime. He fully admitted to his role in her suicide and refused to release the name of the doctor who provided the lethal pills. The public prosecutor used his discretion not to bring charges.

Mr. Humphry was very committed to the issue of assisted suicide. In 1980, he founded the Hemlock Society whose goals were to shed light on the subject and pass legislation that would allow physician-assisted suicide.

Hemlock: In 339 BC, Socrates was put on trial for his political and religious ideas. A jury of 500 peers found him very guilty and condemned him to death. He seemed surprised at the decision, but he took it philosophically. Drinking a cup of hemlock (a poisonous herb commonly found growing by streams) was the method of execution. He drank the cup of brewed hemlock, said goodbye to his friends, rebuked them for their tears, lay down, and became part of history.

By 1991, Mr. Humphry had written another book, *Final Exit: The Practicalities of Self-Deliverance and Assisted Suicide for the Dying.* No commercial publisher would touch his writings. He published his own book with the financial backing of the *Hemlock Society.* There was great interest and a terrific response. *Final Exit* made it to the top of the *New York Times* bestseller list where it remained for 18 weeks. It was also the first self-published book to become an *NYT* bestseller.

His efforts inspired several cottage industries in do-it-yourself do-yourself-in kits.

Sharlotte Hydorn was another early advocate of choice—after her own lengthy experience with the death of her husband, and what she felt was the terrible abuse he suffered at the hands of doctors. Sharlotte was in her nineties and making kits in her own kitchen. She charged $60, which included shipping and postage, and a copy of the book *Final Exit.* Each of the kits was a simple contraption. The method: encasing your head in a plastic bag filed with helium. The kit did not provide the helium source. Helium is lethal in its pure form. This is a quick, certain death.

Good intentions with some tragic outcomes.

Several young, not necessarily fatally ill, but upset and depressed people purchased and used these kits. Clearly, these people needed psychiatric care. The police raided Sharlotte at home. Her kitchen workshop was shut down. Her home was filled with cash and undeposited checks. Money was never her motive. She was not sent to prison. She was sentenced to five years probation for failing to file federal tax forms on her $200,000 from kit sales. Anyway, a year later, she died of natural causes.

Obviously, this was a lousy—if well-intended—project. And undoubtedly, strict guidelines in any assisted suicide are a necessary part of the package.

There was also the well-known doctor named Jack Kevorkian. He helped at least 130 people to leave the planet. He was very fervent and eager to help. Although he was a hero to some, he was a murderer to others. He went to prison for nine years. He could have used some counseling. Sensitive and thoughtful guidelines were missing from his reality. "Dr. Death" was released from prison in 2007, after promising not to help anyone kill themselves. In 2011, when he was 83, Jack Kevorkian died in a hospital very peacefully and without assistance. If you want to spend time with Dr. Death, you can rent the movie, *You Don't Know Jack*, starring Al Pacino.

Oregon, Washington, Vermont and New Mexico have physician-assisted dying laws restricted to terminally ill and mentally competent persons. They have strict guidelines. Yes, I live in New Mexico.

A SUMMARY OF MY LAST THOUGHTS ON THIS SUBJECT:

Do you want to leave a very nasty mess for someone to clean up?

No! Then do not shoot yourself, strangle yourself, or slash your wrists.

Do no harm. Do not drive into a railroad train or another car. You do not want to take anyone out who has not signed on for the trip.

The classic: Hemlock, although it may be available for free in your neighborhood, produces hours of vomiting and painful cramps before it reaches your heart and shuts you down.

No Plath. Do not put your head in the oven. Haven't you spent enough time in the kitchen?

Please, no drama. Do not jump off a bridge or a tall building. These incidents are traumatic for local law enforcement, Search and Rescue crews and random witnesses.

Simple: Stop eating.

Devious: Collect prescription sleeping pills and pain pills.

Metaphysical: Will yourself to die. Contact your local guru.

You may want a great deal more information on this subject than this guide can give you.

Today, there are many organizations that are involved in this discussion such as: Compassion & Choices, Death with Dignity National Center, Final Exit Network, and the World Federation of Right to Die Societies.

You may want to contact an organization. Or join a group. Or start a group.

How is this issue affecting the medical community? Surprise. In the world that listens to the National Institute of Health and controls medical insurance, hospitals and doctors, there is the genuine beginning of a shift in consciousness.

One of the main reasons may be financial. $$$$! What? It is the fantastic cost of acute care given to end-of-time patients. Putting old people on expensive machines in intensive-care units in hospital for lengthy periods of time is beginning to seem financially untenable. David Walker, Co-Chair of the Institute of Medicine's End of Life panel is willing to say, "The system is broke."

Health insurance—perhaps a misnomer—sick insurance—is being burdened by dealing with *senescence*. Cost will drive change.

Some of the radical new thinking:

Insurance companies are being encouraged to pay doctors to talk to their patients about end-of-life care and to listen to the patients' emotions about aging and death. ***Dialogue.***

The medical system is being asked to find ways to allow most people to have their wish of dying at home. ***Peace.***

There may be a change in the medical viewpoint. Encouraging real "health" maintenance. Doctors could promote genuine preventive and pro-active measures that focus on a higher quality of life, not just an extension of life. ***Education.***

More and more doctors are taking a more lenient and loving use of palliative care to provide comfort and ease to the dying patient. ***Compassion.***

Stayed tuned.

End times come in many forms. Sometimes, a person lies down at night in their bed and never wakes up in the morning. A blessing. The final failure of their body system is so quiet that it shuts down gently without even waking their partner who is lying next to them. I woke up early in the morning of April 27th, 2001 to find the still and unoccupied body of my husband. Michael was only 57. He looked quite peaceful. Yes, all of us knew that Michael had stretched his ability to remain alive to its very limit, yet I was shocked and grieved that he had left us.

Death is a powerful and emotionally laden subject. Death is universal—yet for each of us—it is unique and personal.

There are times (often unexpected) that I will find myself thinking about my husband's passing. There are other moments (I may not know why) when I remember the weekend my mother danced her last dance.

My mother's death was, in its own way, a profound experience. Pinky was a complex person and really a very modern woman. She was married four times. She was very different than the mothers of my friends. She had a career. Pinky supported a household of four. She studied yoga and Pilates in the 1940s. She advocated organic food in the 1950s. Definitely sexually liberated. And an early feminist. Much of my life I struggled to understand her. We were not close. And yet....

I feel grateful that my mother knew that her life was coming to an end. I respect her. She was very brave. I am proud of myself that I could honor her decision. Let us all honor and respect each other's choices.

Birth, life, and death are a natural progression.

250

Rain falls in the desert. A rainbow arches over the still valley. The enduring seeds have been waiting. The desert blooms. The seeds scatter. Hiding. Longing for rain. Rain falls....

**

We have reached the end of this guide. I have no more to say, or rather, to write. I hope I been able to shed light on difficult topics. After all my delving in the challenges of aging, dying and death, I still feel more like an explorer than an expert. I hope you found some interesting questions to think about, and even enlightened solutions to your own issues.

My last questions for all of us:

Can we discover more joy and delight in our last days?

Can we celebrate and enrich what is left of our time?

The journey continues.

Continuing the Conversation

Suggested Readings:

Final Exit (the Practicalities of Self-Deliverance and Assisted Suicide for the Dying) written by Derek Humphry, published by Delta.

This is a *how-to* book. That is right. This is a *how-to-kill-yourself* book with illustrations and shopping lists. It is written with compassion and care. You might find it a tough read. I did. This book is forthright and honest. A game-changing and brave effort that is now a classic read.

Death (What should we believe about the nature of death? How should the knowledge of our mortality affect the way we live?) written by Shelly Kagan, published by Yale University Press.

I found this book brutally intellectual. The struggle to grapple with difficult concepts does have value. It does get you thinking. In these pages you will actually find the best argument against suicide from a non-religious viewpoint that I have ever read. I believe that I understood the author to be subtly encouraging his audience to choose quality of life rather than an extended lifetime. Hmm. This is a book by a scientist who does *not* believe in any religion or any form of a spiritual practice. However, he definitely appreciates being alive. His look at defining what life is absolutely shook me up. Definitely *Death* (the book) was a mental challenge: my synapses were snapping and my neurons expanded.

Dying Well (Peace and Possibilities at the End of Life) written by Ira Byock, published by M.D., Riverhead Books.

The book was all heart. I wept over each story of his dying patients. He advocates dealing with our final chapter with honesty, closure, and emotional resolution.

Useful Websites:

www.amodernwomansguide.com

You can always go to my website to download extra journal forms and to learn anything new I have learned about preparing for the final chapter.

You may want to know a great deal more about end-of-life choices. Here is a great start: *www.deathwithdignity.org*

Do you want to chat about end-of-life issues, meet good folks, and have tea and a snack? Here is helpful place to start in your journey to reconcile your attitude towards death: *deathcafe.com*

A time may come that you will need more information about hospice care.

Go to: *www.hospicenet.org*

Lunch with Meaning

This is an exercise that I have created as a gentle way to help us reconcile ourselves to the knowledge our lifespan has an ending. Most of us, when we focus on the meaning of our own story, are surprised by what is truly important to us. I found that having lunch with friends and writing our own obituaries, contrary to what you might expect, was a very enjoyable experience.

WHAT YOU NEED TO DO THIS EXERCISE:

- 4 to 8 willing friends: *Send them an invitation a couple weeks in advance by email or snail mail. You may want to reconfirm a few days before the event.*

- A place with chairs, a table and space (your home, probably).

- Small notebooks for each of them (usually on sale somewhere).

- Pens (8 to 10).

- Lunch for your group (bought, catered or prepared by you). *Please include desert, tea and coffee. When you send out invitation to your friends, it is wise to inquire as to their food allergies or preferences. Everyone, these days, seems to have foods they avoid or are allergic to.*

- Tissue box.

- Straight pins

- 10 sheets of paper, each with the name of a famous deceased woman.

To prepare for the exercise, you will need to select eight to ten famous women who are deceased and create a printed page for each of them.

With the modern tools available to me (i.e.: a computer, a printer and Wikipedia), I easily compiled ten sheets to be used in this exercise. On my list were: Marilyn Monroe, Joan of Arc, Joan Rivers, Eleanor Roosevelt, and other distinguished women that I thought all my friends would recognize. Here is an example of what I pinned to the back of each of my guests:

ELEANOR ROOSEVELT: (according to Wikipedia):

Anna Eleanor Roosevelt (October 11, 1884 – November 7, 1962) was an American politician, diplomat, and activist. She was the longest-serving First Lady of the United States, holding the post from March 1933 to April 1945 during her husband President Franklin D. Roosevelt's four terms in office. President Harry S. Truman later called her the "First Lady of the World" in tribute to her human rights achievements. A member of the Roosevelt and Livingston families, Eleanor had an unhappy childhood, suffering the deaths of both parents and one of her brothers at a young age. At 15, she attended Allenwood Academy in London, and was deeply influenced by its feminist headmistress Marie Souvestre. Returning to the U.S., she married her fifth cousin once removed, Franklin Delano Roosevelt, in 1905. The Roosevelts' marriage was complicated from the beginning by Franklin's controlling mother, Sara, and after discovering Franklin's affair with Lucy Mercer in 1918, Eleanor resolved to seek fulfillment in a public life of her own. She persuaded Franklin to stay in politics following his partial paralysis from polio, and began to give speeches and campaign in his place. After Franklin's election as Governor of New York, Eleanor regularly made public appearances on his behalf. She also shaped the role of First Lady during her tenure and beyond.

Though widely respected in her later years, Roosevelt was a controversial First Lady for her outspokenness, particularly her stance on racial issues. She was the first presidential spouse to hold press conferences, write a syndicated newspaper column, and speak at a national convention. On a few occasions, she publicly disagreed with her husband's policies. She launched an experimental community at Arthurdale, West Virginia, for the families of unemployed miners, later widely regarded as a failure. She advocated for expanded roles for women in the workplace, the civil rights of African Americans and Asian Americans, and the rights of World War II refugees.

Following her husband's death, Eleanor remained active in politics for the rest of her life. She pressed the United States to join and support the United Nations and became one of its first delegates. She served as the first chair of the UN Commission on Human Rights, and oversaw the drafting of the Universal Declaration of Human Rights. Later she chaired the John F. Kennedy administration's Presidential Commission on the Status of Women. By the time of her death, she was regarded as "one of the most esteemed women in the world"; she was called "the object of almost universal respect" in her *New York Times* obituary.[3] In 1999, she was ranked ninth in the top ten of Gallup's List of Most Widely Admired People of the 20th Century.

To begin: Yes, each of your guests is going to have a name pinned to their back. As your guests arrive, you will let each of them choose one sheet (show them the blank side), and you will pin this sheet to their back.

The game: Each guest needs to discover who they are by asking _yes_ or _no_ questions. Avoid any hints. _You have not told your guests that they are famous dead women._ As the leader, a friendly deadpan expression is best. Let your guest mill or sit around and quiz each other.

An example: Susan asks Mandy, "Am I a movie star?" Since the name on her back is Eleanor Roosevelt, Mandy answers, "No."

Another example: Mandy has Joan Rivers pinned to her back. Mandy asks Julia, "Am I a writer?" Julia answers, "Yes." Joan Rivers was a writer as well as a comedian, so the answer is "yes"; however, Mandy may find this confusing as Joan Rivers was best known as a comedian.

Whatever. There are challenges to every game. Encourage your friends to play it straight—hints or clues are not needed. This game should be quite easy to play. And it is a great facilitator to get people comfortable with each other.

Next, serve lunch or allow your guests to serve themselves from a buffet. Have your guests continue to ask questions as you serve lunch. Allow the game to ebb and flow as people eat their food. Eventually, someone will say, "I am Eleanor Roosevelt," and if this is correct, then take the sheet off her back, but ask her to hold onto it.

When lunch is finished, you will want to conclude the game with everyone knowing who they are. If someone is stuck, you (as the leader) may have to give creative hints.

An example of creatively helping your guest to figure out who she is: Linda had Queen Elizabeth I pinned to her back. Linda had figured out that she was a political figure from Europe who lived a long time ago.

She just could not name herself. Finally I asked everyone to treat her if she (the Queen) was here. Everyone curtsied, and then Linda immediately knew she was Queen Elizabeth I.

Lunch (serve desert later) is over. Form an informal circle. Have a discussion with everyone. Ask your friends, "What did these famous or infamous women have in common?" This will produce an interesting and lively discourse. Good. Ideas are flowing. Okay. The conversation goes on. You may have to tell them that besides all the commonalities mentioned, _all these women are deceased._

Next step—Write an epitaph:

An epitaph is an inscription on a tombstone or a short phrase meant to summarize the qualities of the dearly departed. It's a commemorative and short paragraph or a few pithy sentences.

Ask everyone to write an epitaph for her famous person. They can use to information on the sheet of paper or anything they know or feel about this identity.

Here is an example of an epitaph. Linda for Queen Elizabeth I: _A Queen wed to no man, faithful to her country for 40 years._

Or Mandy for Joan Rivers: _Joan grew old without a wrinkle, her wit a keen sword as she won the day for women comedians._

Hand out pens. Give everyone a few minutes to write an epitaph for her famous (now found-out) identity. Now share. Change papers—get them to write another epitaph—share or not.

Next—Dessert, anyone? Coffee or tea?

Writing your personal obituary: THIS EXERCISE IS THE HEART OF THE MATTER.

Introducing this is a bit delicate. You are going to ask everyone to write her own obituary, or what she would like to be read at her funeral, end-of-life celebration or memorial.

This is how I introduced this exercise: I read my mother's obituary from *The New York Times.* You might select an obituary of someone you knew or read a piece that is well written or unusual or even amusing.

My mother was really not famous enough for her death to be chronicled in *The New York Times.* However, a former student was the art critic for the *Times.* She arranged for and wrote this obituary. It would have pleased my mother. Sometimes, just knowing the right person....

Beatrice Lees, Dance Teacher, 84

Beatrice Lees, an innovative teacher of improvisational dance movement, died on Monday at Lenox Hill Hospital. She was 84 and lived in Manhattan.

Mrs. Lees, whose original name was Beatrice Mills, was born in 1910 in Chicago into a theatrical family that included her sister, Viola Spolin, who helped found the improvisational theater movement, and a cousin, Robert Fizdale, the pianist and writer.

Trained in flamenco, modern dance and ballet, she taught movement to non-dance performers, including opera singers, musicians and actors. From 1948 to 1953, she had her own dance company in Chicago. She moved to New York City in 1953 and taught at her own studio until her death.

For the last seven years, Mrs. Lees also taught movement classes and worked on productions at the New Actors Workshop, which was founded in 1988 by Paul Sills, her nephew; Mike Nichols, and George Morrison.

Mrs. Lees was married four times, most recently to Jesse Lees, who died in 1975.

She is survived by a daughter, Claire Haye, and two granddaughters, all of Taos, N.M.

After reading this to my luncheon guests, I suggested that my mother might not have chosen these words for herself and certainly would have emphasized different aspects of her life. If you read a selected obituary, then ask your friends what they felt about what you read them. Moving on.

Next step: Now you can hand out the notebooks and pens for the writing exercise. Let everyone find a comfortable spot to write.

Let us all take the opportunity to write our own last statement. If you were to write your own obituary, what would it say? What are the highlights of your life? What would you like someone to know about you or not know about you? You might want to write your history (brief), or you might choose to give advice to the next generation. There are many different ways to fulfill this assignment.

Your friends may ask for detailed instructions. As the coach, try to keep this experience as *open* and *unstructured* as possible. Give your group permission to write anything that the topic inspires. There are no rules: you can use any form or voice or style that comes to mind.

Give everyone no more than 15 minutes to complete the exercise.

Provide tissue. When one person has finished, then it is time to give the group five more minutes. Yes, you need to write your obituary as well.

Time is up. Form some kind of circle.

Now ask your group, "Does anyone want to read what they wrote?" Or, "Alice, would you share your writing?" Or if no one else is willing, you can always read your own piece. Start and then continue around the circle. You want to encourage everyone to read what she wrote.

I am always surprised and touched by what women have to say.

Concluding:

Ask the group:

What did you learn about yourself?

How did you feel about doing this exercise?

What surprised you about what you said?

Spend as much or little time in follow-up discussion as feels right.

Finally: hugs, and appreciation. Yes, send everyone home with their notebooks and leftover food.

What needs doing or completing? Beyond the Bucket List

We realize our time is limited. Are we leaving something undone? Places to see? Bridges to cross? People to see? Treks that need slogging? Making a list of journeys, experiences, or personal reconciliations, and then completing them one by one (and crossing them off our list), has become a popular pastime. Everyone is making a bucket list. Heavyweight movie stars (think Jack Nicolson and Morgan Freeman) entertain us with portrayals of men rising from their hospital beds to go for crazy adventures and heartfelt reunions. What about you? Do you think you can formulate a plan that would fulfill your sense of having lived to the max?

Yes, if it suits you, and you have the budget, *getting to the finish line with honor* can be about going to special places, making amends, doing it up, and fabulous meals. And if all of us started running around the world with pen and paper, this could be a terrific boon for the travel industry.

This might be a great way to use the remaining time on the clock. Very few of us know how long that will be. Or how long we will have the energy to zip around the world. Or make things right with people we care about.

Do you like making lists? I think that that there is value in making lists. Don't you? This could be exciting. Let us start.

$$$$ Small and most likely pricey stuff you have always longed for or wanted to do:

Do you want to have a day at premiere spa, an expensive dress for a one-time occasion, a diamond ring, or dinner at a five-star restaurant? What minor (money is meant to be used) indulgences have you been depriving yourself of that could amuse, entertain or cheer you up? Go ahead, darling—have at it. As for me, I am signing up for oysters, fresh lobster, and corn-on-the-cob. All the melted butter I want.

1._____

2._____

3._____

4._____

More:_____

$ or $$$ Clearing your personal slate:

Many of us have experienced the loss of friends and family who are alive, but for very various reasons have become "dead" to us. Is there some way to dredge the swamp, start over, or express anger or regret? Take a chance, write a letter, or make a phone call—be the bigger heart.
I agree that there may some relationships that can never be healed. Light a candle, think kind thoughts, or plant a tree. Very serious and destructive relationships that caused permanent harm may never have a simple solution. You could consider donating time and/or money to a cause that seems to address the issue.

$ or $$$$$$$$ Leaving your legacy:

More than 20,000 years ago, Neolithic artists dipped their hands in red ochre and pressed them on cave walls. Their crimson handprints are still visible. Amazing.

Do you wish to leave a mark—small or grand?

Let us think helpful. Is there something you could do to better the world you leave behind? Making positive and innovative changes in how you are spending your last energies may make a difference in the meaning of your entire life and leave an important legacy behind.

Any great ideas?

Sometime later.

Wow, you have crossed everything off your list. Having done it all, are you more at ease with your eventual demise? Or have you discovered your quest to find peace with death is a more esoteric and subtle journey done from the inside radiating outwards?

264

Thoughts.......

Thoughts.......

Thoughts.......

Thoughts.......

Thoughts.......

Thoughts.......

Appendices:

Thirteen Rights - A Global Bill of Rights for Women
www.13rights.com

*Thirteen Rights is a testimony created by the **W**orldwide **W**omen's **I**ntegrated Socie-ty for **E**veryone and **E**verything (WWISEE) to ensure that every female born any-where people live will be entitled to and possess as her birthright all the following freedoms and protections as set forth in this Global Bill of Rights for Women.*

*The **Truth:** I, Claire Haye, am "Wwisee". I wrote this Bill of Rights in 2010 as a proclamation to the world: **Women are equal to men and deserve inherently all the same rights that men everywhere claim as their birthright.** It was important to me to put in writing what I would like to see put into practice everywhere.*

We wise women have declared that is our mission is to make these laws in their full and complete expression, the laws of every land everywhere, and for these laws, in their entirety, to be fully enforced and followed by all human societies. We wise women contend that freeing women in all societies will be for the betterment of our species and the earth itself. We invite all men and women of the earth to join us in providing and upholding these laws. We hold that these rights of women need to be declared and made law in all lands of the earth.

1. **We claim the right to vote in all elections.** The laws of every country will provide safe, free, and available access to voting facilities.

2. **We claim equal representation in the government.** Women shall be

part and party to the functioning of the government of their country. This includes, but is not limited to, equal representation in the governing bodies of businesses, banks, financial businesses, and the military.

3. **We claim the right to assemble and access to communication.** Women have the right to gather in groups without male supervision or approval, and we have the right of and access to communication with any person or organization. We claim free and unsupervised access to all methods of communication.

4. **We declare that females will be educated equally to the males in every society in terms of quality, scholarship, access, and duration.** Education is to include athletic participation. Females will have complete access to sports facilities and equal rights to train and compete. Education is to include the arts, the right to perform these arts, and the access to public space for the performance or display of all art forms. Funds for education, athletics, and the arts for females will be spent in equal amounts to the funds spent on males.

5. **We claim freedom of movement.** Females have the right to drive any vehicle that any man is allowed to drive. We claim the right to go anywhere in or out of our country without permission or consent of another person. We claim the right to own vehicles in our own name, and the right to be licensed to drive by oneself—without male interference or supervision—any vehicle any man is licensed to drive. We demand safe and free access to all facilities that provide such licenses.

6. **We claim freedom of marriage or non-marriage—that is the right to self-select a mate or a lover.** We claim the right to our sexual expression, in or out of marriage, with a male or a female partner. Neither minor females nor adult women can be married as part of contracts that have been arranged *for* her and not *by* her. Nor can any woman or female child be sold or traded into sexual or domestic slavery. Women claim the right to exit a marriage or a marriage-like arrangement. We claim the right to divorce, and in the event of divorce, the right to an equal share of property, investments, and goods. In regards to the children born into any union, we will have the right to keep our children in our domain, equal access to the children, and the right to raise these children, as we deem appropriate.

7. **We claim the right to carry weapons for protection against rape.** Provisions will be made in the laws everywhere to allow self-defense against rape, physical harm to a woman's person, or that of her family. Acts of self-defense will be not result in persecution or retribution, even if the female's actions result in the injury or death of her assailant.

8. **We claim the right to own property.** Every woman has the right to own property entirely under her own power and in her own name. Property includes—but is not limited to—houses, cars, and commercial businesses. Every woman also has the right to do business on her own and in her own name. We claim the right to sell or transfer property, as we deem necessary.

9. **We claim the right to work** at any occupation that men can be employed at and to be paid at the same rate that our male counterpart would be paid. We claim equal rights and access to the public workplace.

10. **We claim the right to the physical appearance of own choosing.** By this we mean that is every female can appear in public in clothing, adornment, or cosmetics of her own choosing without retribution by the laws or customs of that society.

11. **We claim the right to birth control** and fair, affordable, and reasonable access to all information concerning birth control as well as to the actual methods of birth control.

12. **We claim the right to safely terminate a pregnancy** and the fair, affordable, and safe access to methods and facilities that aid in the termination of any pregnancy. Conversely, we claim the right to keep and raise any child that we have given birth to, in or out of legal marriage.

13. **We claim the right of sanctity of our female genitals.** In no human society will it be legal to mutilate or alter the genitals or any other body part of any grown woman or female child.

Bibliography

I fully acknowledge my debt to other authors and sincerely declare my appreciation for their research and ideas.

Assante, Julia. *The Last Frontier: Exploring the Afterlife and Transforming Our Fear of Death.* Novato, CA: New World Library, 2012.

Bolen, Jean Shinoda, *Crones Don't Whine: Concentrated Wisdom for Juicy Women.* York Beach, ME: Conari Press, 2003.

Bowman, Tracey and Mary Boone Wellington. *Hope I Don't Die Before I Get Old: How to Survive Old Age, Your Own or Someone You Love.* Nashua, NH: Rose Cottage Publishing, 2012.

Brenton, Maria. *Choice, Autonomy and Mutual Support: Older Women's Collaborative Living Arrangements.* York, UK: York Publishing Services, 1999.

Brizendine, Louann. *The Female Brain.* New York: Random House, 2006.

Buettner, Dan. *The Blue Zones (Second Edition): 9 Lessons for Living Longer from the People Who've Lived the Longest.* Washington, D.C.: National Geographic Society, 2012.

Byock, Ira. *Dying Well: Peace and Possibilities at the End of Life.* New York:Riverhead Books, 1998.

Carroll, Sean B. *The Making of the Fittest: DNA and the Ultimate Forensic Record of Evolution.* New York: Norton, 2007.

Crowley, Chris and Henry S. Lodge. *Younger Next Year for Women: Live Strong, Fit, and Sexy–Until You're 80 and Beyond.* New York: Workman Publishing, 2007.

Erikson, Erik H. and Joan M. Erikson. *The Life Cycle Completed: Extended Version with New Chapters on the Ninth Stage of Development.* New York: Norton, 1998.

Erikson, Erik H., Joan M. Erikson, and Helen Q. Kivnick. *Vital Involvement in Old Age.* New York: Norton, 1994.

Friedman, Howard S., and Leslie R. Martin. *The Longevity Project: Surprising Discoveries for Health and Long Life from the Landmark Eight-Decade Study.* New York: Penguin, 2012.

Gladwell, Malcolm. *Blink: The Power of Thinking Without Thinking.* New York: Little, Brown & Co., 2005.

Gladwell, Malcolm. *Outliers: The Story of Success.* New York: Little, Brown & Co., 2011.

Grisanti, Jen. *Change Your Story, Change Your Life: A Path to Success.* Studio City, CA: Divine Arts, 2013.

Hayflick, Leonard. *How and Why We Age.* New York: Ballantine, 1994.

Humphry, Derek. *Final Exit: The Practicalities of Self-Deliverance and Assisted Suicide for the Dying.* New York: Delta, 2010.

Jacoby, Susan. *Never Say Die: The Myth and Marketing of the New Old Age.* New York: Pantheon, 2011.

Kagan, Shelly. *Death.* The Open Yale Courses Series. New Haven & London: Yale University Press, 2012.

Kubler-Ross, Elisabeth. *On Death & Dying: What the Dying Have to Teach Doctors, Nurses, Clergy and Their Own Families.* New York: Scribner, 2014.

LeMaitre, George D., *How to Choose a Good Doctor.* Bloomington, IN: AuthorHouse, 2006.

Lieberman, Daniel E. *The Evolution of the Human Head*. Cambridge & London: Belknap of Harvard U. Press, 2011.

Lieberman, Daniel E. *The Story of the Human Body: Evolution, Health and Disease*. New York: Pantheon, 2013.

Matten, Glen and Aidan Goggins. *The Health Delusion: How to Achieve Exceptional Health in the 21st Century*. Alexandria: Hay House Australia,Ltd., 2012.

Nelson, Miriam E. with Sarah Wernick. *Strong Women Stay Young*. New York: Bantam, 1997.

Nuland, Sherwin B. *How We Die: Reflections on Life's Final Chapter*. New York: Vintage, 1995.

Orman, Suze. *The 9 Steps to Financial Freedom: Practical & Spiritual Steps So You Can Stop Worrying*. New York: Three Rivers Press, 1997.

Pollan, Michael. *Food Rules: An Eater's Manual*. New York: Penguin, 2009.

Pollan, Michael. *The Omnivore's Dilemma: A Natural History of Four Meals*. New York: Penguin, 2007.

Richerson, Peter J. and Robert Boyd. *Not by Genes Alone: How Culture Transformed Human Evolution*. Chicago: U. of Chicago Press, 2005.

Ridley, Matt. *Genome: The Autobiography of a Species in 23 Chapters*. New York: Harper Perennial, 2006.

Ridley, Matt. *The Red Queen: Sex and the Evolution of Human Nature*. New York: Penguin, 1993.

Rubin, Gretchen. *The Happiness Project*. New York: HarperCollins, 2011.

Saxon, Sue V., Mary Jean Etten, and Elizabeth A. Perkins. *Physical Change and Aging: A Guide for the Helping Professions*. New York: Springer, 2010.

Sell, Christina. *Yoga from the Inside Out: Making Peace with Your Body Through Yoga.* Prescott, AZ: Hohm Press, 2003.

Snowden, David. *Aging with Grace: What the Nun Study Teaches Us About Leading Longer, Healthier and More Meaningful Lives.* New York: Bantam, 2001.

Staton, Jana, Roger Shuy, and Ira Byock. *A Few Months to Live: Different Paths to Life's End.* Washington, D.C.: Georgetown U. Press, 2001.

Sykes, Bryan. *Adams's Curse: A Future Without Men.* New York: Norton, 2004.

About Claire Haye:

Claire Haye is a well-known visual artist. She has lived in Taos, New Mexico since 1978. She came here as a young woman with her husband and two small daughters. Time has passed, she has become a grandmother, a widow and a senior citizen. For nearly two decades, she has owned her own gallery, *Claireworks*, in the charming mountain village of Arroyo Seco, New Mexico. Claire has had considerable success with her original jewelry and fine art.

Claire loves the independence that her gallery has provided her. She lives in a beautiful rambling adobe house surrounded by piñon and juniper trees. Her nearest neighbors are rabbits, ravens and an occasional skunk. Sometimes she is lonely and restless, but most often she is fully occupied by her many art projects. Last year she completed a large ceramic mural as well as a dozen new jewelry designs. You can view her work at *www.claireworks.com*.

Writing *A Modern Woman's Guide to Aging* has been a departure from Claire's more recognized pursuits as a painter, sculptor and jeweler. Her art collectors may be quite surprised that Claire has written a guide to aging. They never knew her as the intellectual young girl who read five books a week, the serious student of science or over the years as an author of curiously dark poetry.

A conversation between Claire and her friend Jane gave birth to the idea of writing about issues specific to aging women. The project resonated more with Claire than Jane. Surprise. After two years, considerable reading, research, writing, and editing Claire produced this volume. For her this has been a fascinating journey of learning and acceptance. Now that the guide is finished, Claire has the time and the fervent desire to implement her own recommendations.